MW00616001

TUKY

The Story of a Hidden Child

by Shterni Rosenfeld
illustrations by Jacky Yarhi

Based on true events
in the life of Mrs. Tuky Treitel

Hachai
PUBLISHING

Tuky

The Story of a Hidden Child

To my constant inspirations... Anyu z"l,
my father, Yeshaya Aryeh ben Menashe z"l,
and in honor of my mother, Tuky, תלחט"א
whose courage I will always admire. S. R.

First Edition – Cheshvan 5775 / November 2015
Hardcover ISBN: 978-1-929628-85-8

Softcover Edition – Kislev 5776 / December 2016
Softcover ISBN: 978-1-945560-01-9

Copyright © 2015 by HACHAI PUBLISHING
ALL RIGHTS RESERVED

Editor: D.L. Rosenfeld
Managing Editor: Yossi Leverton
Layout: Moshe Cohen

LCCN: 2015943144

HACHAI PUBLISHING
Brooklyn, N.Y.
Tel: 718-633-0100   Fax: 718-633-0103
www.hachai.com - info@hachai.com

Table of Contents

❦ ❦ ❦

The events in this story are true, but some conversations
and characters were added or altered for clarity.

Meet the Main Characters

 Apu — The father of Tuky's family, Apu does his best to save his children from the Nazis.

 Anyu — A gentle, courageous woman, Tuky's mother always trusts in Hashem. Together with Apu, she opens their home to those in need.

 Tuky — A bright, charming girl of six who looks out for her brother and cousin during the war.

 Misu — Tuky's younger brother, this five-year-old boy relies on his big sister when they are away from home.

 Puncsi — This young boy is Tuky's cousin whom she looks after.

Tuky's Family

Father: (Apu)
Lezer Dovid

Mother: (Anyu)
Golda/Gizi

Children:

Hindi	Frédi
Mirca	Miki
Sami	Zigi
Tuky (Malka)	Ziszi
Misu	Ezriel
Zsuzsa	

Uncle:
Colev bácsi

Aunt:
Terus néni

Tuky's cousins:

Hindi	Puncsi
Babu	Bandi
Maki	Márta
Sami	Erika
Bozi	

Hungarian Words

Tuky and her family lived in Budapest, Hungary and spoke the Hungarian language. This list will help you understand some of the Hungarian words that appear in Tuky's story.

Apu .... Father

Anyu................. Mother

Bácsi (ba-chee).....Uncle (used after the person's name, as if saying, Colev-Uncle)

Néni (nay-nee).....Aunt (used after the person's name, as if saying, Terus-Aunt)

Né .... Mrs. (used after the last name, as if saying, Kohn-Mrs.)

Úr .... Mr. (used after the last name, as if saying, Ladics-Mr.)

Szervusz .... Hello

Pengö .... Unit of Hungarian money

Chapter One

"Tuky, what ARE you doing?"

Tuky giggled. She was standing on her head, enjoying the upside down view of her room. The ceiling looked like a floor, with the light fixture standing straight up instead of hanging down.

From that position, her big sister, Mirca, looked so funny!

"Honestly, Tuky, aren't you too old for headstands?"

For upside down Tuky, Mirca's disapproving frown curled up like a cheerful smile.

"I'll never be too old to stand on my head," she answered firmly. "Never!"

"Come on, Tuky! Stand up! Your first

lesson is today."

Tuky flopped over and stood on her feet, waiting for the blood to rush back down from her face. She'd almost forgotten! Today she would learn how to embroider material with fancy stitches. Her mother was going to show her how to decorate a handkerchief with flowers and leaves and all kinds of beautiful designs!

Tuky skipped to the front room and bent over her little work basket, marveling at the colorful spools of thread inside. Her mother, whom all the children called 'Anyu,' was waiting patiently.

"Please," said her mother, "pick a color so we can begin your lesson."

"Oh, Anyu, you choose! I can't wait to start!"

Anyu smiled at her daughter's enthusiasm. That was her Tuky, always full of joy, excited about learning to embroider her very own handkerchief, the happiest girl in Budapest.

"Well, what about blue? You like blue, don't you?"

"Oh, yes," Tuky answered, admiring a spool of sky-colored thread. "But this red is so bright. Maybe I should start with red! After all, it is my favorite."

Anyu laughed. "That's fine with me! There are so many colors in this pattern, that you'll be able to give each one a chance. Watch the way I thread the needle and make nice tight stitches."

Tuky watched her mother's every move, then took the embroidery hoop to give it a try. After a few red stitches that were too loose, and a few more that were too tight, Tuky leaned closer to Anyu to show her work.

"Hmmm," said her mother, "I see you are trying hard, but be careful not to pull the thread so tightly. When you do that, the fabric bubbles up."

Tuky carefully removed the stitches with her needle, one at a time. She smoothed the fabric and started again. Finally she sat back in her chair, sewing comfortably next to her beloved Anyu.

They worked side by side at the light-colored wooden table, where family meals were always served. The large front room was the heart of the house. Tuky loved the small corner sink with running water. She loved the pantry shelves stocked with colorful jars of Anyu's homemade tomato soup, pickled vegetables, prune butter, and apricot jam.

Tuky sighed with happiness. She loved being six. Six was big. Six meant starting school, knowing how to tie her shoes by herself, and learning to embroider like Anyu!

This was a precious time when she could ask her mother anything. In a family with eight children, it was a rare treat to sit and talk alone with her mother in the quiet front room.

"Anyu, tell me again about my name."

Anyu's eyes twinkled as she finished darning a hole in one sock and began on a second one. "What about your name?"

Tuky giggled, then stopped and pulled her needle up and over. "You know… how I got the name Tuky!"

"Well," Anyu said, "six years ago in Hungary, on the first day of Elul, a beautiful baby girl was born. She had black hair, dark eyes, and the cutest smile in the world.

"Her name was Malka Gestetner, but because she was as sweet as sugar, her parents called her *Tzukor*, the Yiddish word for sugar. When her brother Sami tried to say "*Tzukor*," he couldn't quite do it. He called his sister Tuky, and Tuky she was called from that day on!"

"Then what happened?"

Her mother continued, "That baby grew up to become the best little helper on Kolozsvari Street. She brings her father his coffee downstairs in his factory, she helps take care of her little brother and her little cousin, and she's embroidering a colorful handkerchief all by herself!"

Tuky looked up from her flower petal.

"Do you think I'll have this nickname all my life?"

Anyu just smiled. Talking and storytelling made the time fly. Tuky loved the

way her needle poked in and out of the linen cloth, leaving a trail of bright red stitches.

She held up her work to admire it in the sunlight. Glancing out the window Tuky said,

"Look, Anyu! The leaves on our vinegar tree* have turned as red as my thread!"

"You're right, Tuky! No wonder it's your favorite."

Tuky couldn't help taking a break to stare at the gorgeous leaves of her special tree. All summer it provided a green shady spot on their little dead end street. But in the fall, the leaves became a spectacular show of color.

She smiled at the sight of her younger sister, Zsuzsa, and little brother, Frédi, chasing each other around the base of the tree. Tuky felt so much older, now that she could embroider!

Taking up her needle again, Tuky patiently filled in the entire petal, stitch by stitch. Finally it was finished!

With capable hands, Anyu tied a strong, tiny knot to hold the thread in place.

"There," said her mother, snipping off an extra piece with her small scissors. She poked the tiny knot underneath the stitches and out of sight.

*also known as a sumac tree

"The back of your work should look neat and beautiful, just like the front."

Tuky couldn't believe it! She had made her first perfect flower petal, and she couldn't wait to do more.

"Oh Anyu, can I do another petal now?" asked Tuky eagerly.

"I'd love to say yes, *édes kislány*, my sweet little girl, but we have to get ready for supper. Your brothers will be finishing their lessons shortly, and they'll be so hungry."

Standing up, Anyu folded the rest of her mending into her basket. Tuky carefully flattened out her embroidery. With her fingertip, she stroked the smooth bump of her first red petal. The handkerchief design was so detailed. Would she ever finish all those flowers?

"I will," Tuky decided. "I won't give up until it's finished!"

Folding the cloth neatly, she put it in her basket and followed her mother into the kitchen.

Just then, two of Tuky's brothers tumbled into the house. Her older brother Sami, tall with dark hair, and her younger brother Misu, with twinkling eyes, had just returned from their lessons with Reb Yisroel.

Anyu turned around and saw her two big sons. Smiling at them she said, "I hope your lessons went well today. Now go and wash up, Apu will come up soon, and it will be time to eat."

Tuky sighed. Apu would be very tired after work. His factory downstairs was a busy place! There were rolls and rolls of material stacked up against every wall, big machines for creating different colors and patterns on fabric, and lots of workers to fill the orders and make deliveries.

Wiping her hands on her apron, Anyu called Hindi and Mirca, Tuky's two older sisters. Together, the girls came into the front room, laughing and talking. How Tuky admired them! Their dark hair was neatly pulled back into long braids, and their aprons were spotless and crisply starched.

"I embroidered a red flower petal today," Tuky told them proudly.

"Good for you!" said Hindi.

"I remember when Anyu first taught me to embroider," said Mirca. "I thought it was so hard, but compared to the tablecloth I'm working on now, it was easy!"

Tuky's smile faded. No matter what she learned, her older sisters already knew it.

"Now girls," said Anyu, "everyone has to start from the beginning, and I don't think anyone started with as much energy as Tuky! Her red petal is just beautiful."

Tuky felt her smile pop up again. Anyu always knew how to make her feel better.

"Hindi," Anyu continued, "please get the baby; he's up from his nap. Mirca, run and get the children from outside and wash their hands and faces. Tuky, it's time to set the table."

Everyone listened right away. In Tuky's

family, no one ever complained or kept Anyu waiting. Everyone had to help with chores.

Just as Tuky laid the last fork on the flowered tablecloth, she heard Apu's footsteps coming up the stairs. How strong and tall he was, and how happy Tuky was to see him! She ran to be the first to give Apu a kiss on his hand, then a kiss on his cheek. All the children welcomed their father this way.

Apu pinched Tuky's cheeks fondly and smiled at her, his gold tooth winking in the light. Nothing made Tuky feel warmer inside than seeing her father's shiny gold smile.

"*Szervusz*, Apu," Tuky's mother greeted Apu with a traditional Hungarian 'hello.' "Come and sit down, so we can eat the soup while it is nice and hot."

The children waited respectfully for their father to wash his hands for bread. Then one by one, they lined up at the sink in the corner, washed and said the *brocha*.

After Apu made *Hamotzi* on the fresh rye bread, the meal began. Anyu served Apu first, giving him a steaming bowl of mushroom soup with a fluffy knaidel. Then she served each of the children.

Tuky looked around the table at her family. It was a wonderful time of day when they all sat down together to eat Anyu's delicious food. Hindi took small ladylike bites. Mirca helped Zsuzsa cut up her knaidel. Sami and Misu were always starving after a long day of learning and had to be reminded to slow down. Anyu sat with baby Miki on her lap and Frédi at her side. Lovingly, she fed her two youngest their soup, spoonful by spoonful.

As Tuky ate her supper, she listened to her parents speak. She wanted to tell her father about the red petal she'd made, but children never interrupted when the adults were talking. And lately, it seemed that all they ever talked about was news of the war.

"No one is sure," Apu said, "but there are rumors that the Nazis will march in and take over Hungary next."

Anyu spooned more soup into Zsuzsa's mouth and murmured, "May *Hashem Yisborach* protect us all."

Tuky knew that Nazis were German soldiers, but she wasn't really paying attention. On that fall day in 1943, war sounded far away. What could it possibly have to do with her family here on Kolozsvari Street?

Happily, she turned her attention back to her own bowl of mushroom soup and the lovely knaidel floating on top.

Chapter Two

Early the next morning, Tuky awoke and said *Modeh Ani.* From her bed, she saw the sun peeking through the starched white curtains.

"Oh, good!" she thought. "It looks like a beautiful day!"

Quickly, Tuky washed *negel vasser,* got dressed, and put on her favorite apron. It was made of blue fabric with a white half-moon pattern that Apu had dyed in his factory. Then Tuky squeezed her feet into her high brown leather shoes. Starting from the bottom, she tightened her laces until each shoe fit snugly on her foot and hugged her ankle. Carefully, she pulled the laces and tied them into nice, neat bows. Now she was ready to start her day!

Just then, there was a knock at the door. Who could it possibly be so early in the morning? Of course; today was Monday. Monday was always laundry day!

Anyu opened the door. There stood Jultza and Annush, the two washerwomen. They were dressed in plain cotton dresses with large aprons tied in the back. Each wore her hair pulled back in a tight bun, and their hands were red and chapped from scrubbing so much laundry.

"Good day Gestetner né. Is everything ready in the laundry room?"

"Yes. It is all prepared for you," said Anyu. "But first, have some *kávé.*"

This hot, dark brown drink was made of chicory, and it looked and smelled like coffee.

"Thank you, Gestetner né," answered Jultza.

But Annush was anxious to begin. "Let's get to work," she grumbled. "With so many children, and so much laundry, it will be dark before we leave."

Annush opened the door to the laundry room, and sure enough, there was a huge pile of laundry. Clothing of all sizes, tablecloths, handkerchiefs and washing rags were all piled, ready to be scrubbed.

Tuky tiptoed along the porch and peered from behind the door at the two women who were hard at work. They filled a large basin with dirty clothing and poured kettles full of boiling water on top. They scrubbed each garment with a bar of brown soap. Then they swished it all around in the water with their big, strong hands. When the laundry was all soapy, they took out each item and rinsed it again and again in clean, clear water.

Finally, the pile was finished. Together, Jultza and Annush twisted every piece of laundry to wring out most of the water. One by one, they hung the clean things on the clothesline to drip dry in the sun.

Tomorrow, the ironing woman would come and remove all the clothing from the line. She would heat the iron on the stove top and quickly flatten all the wrinkles. *Tsss, Tsss.* The iron would hiss as the ironing woman moved it quickly back and forth. It was a wonder that she didn't burn her fingers!

Tuky's stomach started grumbling. It reminded her that she had not eaten her breakfast yet. She scooted back down to the other end of the porch and walked back inside.

The house smelled of *griz*, a delicious cream of wheat cereal that Anyu always cooked for breakfast. Tuky hurried to the table, where Mirca was dishing out steaming bowls of *griz* for Zsuzsa, Frédi, and little Miki. Anyu was sprinkling the hot, milky *griz* with cocoa and sugar, making beautiful patterns and swirly designs in each bowl.

Sami and Misu were almost finished with their breakfast. Usually, they had to eat quickly and go to the nearby shul to learn with their teacher. Today, Reb Yisroel couldn't come, so the boys were still at home.

"*Kis di hant,* Anyu," Tuky said. That was the proper way to greet an adult.

"Good morning to you, *édes kislány,*" said Anyu. Tuky loved when her mother called her a sweet girl.

Anyu smiled at her. "Come here, Tuky, and I'll fix your hair before davening."

Before she knew it, Tuky's hair was brushed and pinned neatly to one side. How did Anyu's hands move so quickly?

Tuky davened and joined the others at the table. She made a *brocha* and took her first sweet spoonful of *griz.* This morning, Anyu had swirled the cocoa and sugar into a flower! Tuky carefully ate each petal, one by one, and washed it down with sips of *kávé* mixed with rich, creamy milk.

All the children were expected to finish every bit of food put in front of them. That was Anyu's rule, and they never questioned it. Besides, everything she cooked was so delicious, that no one wanted to waste a single bite!

Just as Tuky finished her breakfast, she heard a happy shout from outside. Her cousins, Bozi and Puncsi, were here! Their father was Apu's brother, the uncle she called Colev bácsi. He and Apu were partners in the business, and the two brothers worked together in the factory every day.

As the boys pulled up on their bikes, Tuky and Misu shot a longing glance at their mother.

"Yes," laughed Anyu, "you may go out to play. But take Zsuzsa with you, and keep an eye on her. Don't forget your sweaters!"

Tuky jumped up, grabbed her sweater, and tugged Zsuzsa by the hand. They were so happy that cousins their age lived nearby! Bozi was six and a half, just like Tuky, but taller and stockier than she was. Puncsi, Bozi's lanky little brother was five, just like Misu. They were all best friends and playmates, never lonely and never bored because they had each other. Together they formed a lively group, with three-year-old

Zsuzsa always tagging along.

"Hi Bozi! Want to race? I know I can ride my bike faster than you!" Tuky grinned at her dark, stocky cousin, eager to show him how fast she could pedal.

"I'll race the winner," said Misu.

Bozi grinned. Tuky pulled her bike alongside his. "Let's go!" she shouted. The two bikes flew down the gravel lined street. There was no traffic on their little dead end road, so it was safe to ride there. Small stones bounced and crackled as Bozi pulled ahead. Then, her hair streaming out behind her, Tuky put on a burst of speed, pedaling with all her might. Zsuzsa jumped and cheered.

The courtyard gate was the finish line. Tuky strained to go faster and faster. Finally, she braked, stood up on the pedals, and looked back. She had won!

Bozi stopped and jumped off his bike, breathing heavily. "It was my shoelace. It came untied... slowed me down."

Tuky looked down at her own laced shoes, glad that she'd taken the time to tie them tightly this morning.

"Well, let me fix it," she offered, "and then I'll race Misu!"

The children raced and rode until they were hot and tired. They leaned their bikes against the house, and plopped down under the vinegar tree to decide what to do next.

"We could roll a bike wheel with a stick," said Misu.

"Too tired," said Puncsi. "How about hopscotch?"

"Too hot," said Bozi.

Then Tuky had an idea. "Let's go to the factory!"

They didn't waste a minute. All five children ran across the courtyard and stopped at the factory door. On the doorway was a small white sign with raised black letters. It read: *Gestetner Lajos, Kekfesto es Kartonnyomo*, Gestetner's Cotton Blue Dye Factory.

Bozi, the strongest of the four, pulled back the large door and held it open. "Hurry up," he said.

The children tiptoed into the office. It was quiet there today. They went around the large wooden desk and opened the door leading to the factory floor.

What a busy place! The children stood for a while watching the workers unload rolls and rolls of light-colored cotton material. They were piling it up on large shelves that lined the factory walls.

Sometimes the cousins would run up and down between the long rows, counting the rolls and feeling the different fabrics. On other days, they took cans of dye from the factory and found lots of things to do with them. But today, a new order had arrived, so the children knew that their fathers would want them to keep quiet and out of the way.

"Move aside," bellowed the Hungarian foreman, as he wiped his damp face with a handkerchief. He had worked for Apu for many years. When he first came to Budapest, he met Bözsi, Anyu's Hungarian maid. The two hard workers married and settled down right near 123 Kolozsvari Street.

"These rolls are heavy, and I don't want any to roll on top of you!"

They all stood on the side for a few minutes. But soon Misu and Puncsi tugged at Tuky's sleeve. "Let's go closer!"

Tuky held Zsuzsa's hand and motioned for the others to follow her. They made their way around the large dying vat, where a skinny man with glasses and a brown moustache stood measuring blue dye in a jar. He would soon pour it into the large vat of boiling water to make enough dye to start coloring the material a rich beautiful blue.

He looked up and noticed Tuky first. "Hey there, does your father know you're here?"

Tuky looked down at her shoes. She felt shy when grownups talked to her... even the factory men that she saw all the time. Bozi

answered for her. "We just wanted to see the delivery come in. We won't touch anything!"

"Better not," answered the man, shaking his head.

Walking along like a little parade, the children came to their favorite part of the factory, the centrifuge. It looked like the drum of a washing machine, only much, much bigger! The centrifuge could hold huge amounts of freshly dyed, wet fabric, spinning it around and around until the material was almost dry.

Tuky's eyes sparkled with fun. "Let's pretend that we are wet blue fabric!" She hoisted Zsuzsa into the giant drum and climbed in after her. Tuky smoothed down her blue apron with its small white designs, printed and dyed right here in this factory. Puncsi jumped in, too, and the three of them lay down along the sides of the large machine.

Tuky reached up and pulled the chain. With a wheeze and whir, the drum started turning, slowly at first, then faster and faster!

The children giggled as they spun around and around. Everything looked like one big blur. What a ride!

When it stopped, they peered up, dizzy and laughing, to see Misu and Bozi looking down at them. Tuky knew exactly what they were about to say.

"Our turn!"

Chapter Three

A few weeks later, on a Friday afternoon, Tuky was sitting on the balcony, all buttoned up in her heavy cream-colored sweater. She was trying to embroider her handkerchief and keep an eye on the little children playing below in the courtyard.

Every so often, Tuky stopped to take a deep breath of fresh air and to drink in the bright blue of the sky. The vinegar tree's branches were bare, but it still looked so lovely as it swayed in the chilly fall breeze.

"Misu, stop throwing sticks! You'll hurt Zsuzsa, and then she'll go crying to Anyu!"

"Will not," Zsuzsa protested. "I'm big now."

"Of course you are... ouch!" Tuky had

stuck the needle into her finger. Why couldn't she ever use a thimble the way Anyu did? Tuky pressed her finger on her handkerchief so she wouldn't bleed on the yellow petals. She had finally finished all the red ones and was so glad to be working with thread of a different color.

Anyu was in the kitchen cooking for Shabbos together with the maids. The tempting smells of *challah*, chicken soup with ginger, and spicy *letcho* made with onions, peppers, and tomatoes wafted out the window. In a just a few hours, they'd have all these delicious foods in honor of Shabbos.

Anyu came onto the porch, wiping her hands on her apron.

"Tuky, *édes kislány*, please put away your embroidery, and come inside. I have a special job for you today."

Tuky tucked her handkerchief into a small basket and followed her mother through the front room and into the kitchen. There, Bözsi the maid was putting some

Shabbos fish, cooked chicken, and fresh *challah* loaves into a basket.

"You remember that our neighbor, Kohn né, had a little boy two weeks ago, and Apu was the *mohel*? Well, I've been helping her with the baby and bringing her food, but I just can't leave now. Today I am busy preparing for Shabbos. Would you be a big girl and do this mitzvah?"

Tuky stood up tall. She couldn't believe it. These jobs were usually given to Hindi or Mirca, and now Anyu was trusting her!

Anyu continued, "Make sure when you get there to unpack the food and set up for Shabbos. Tell Kohn né that you will watch the baby so that she can lie down for a nap. Remember to keep your arm under the baby's head when you hold him."

Anyu took a twenty pengö note and placed in Tuky's apron pocket. Tuky had never been in charge of that much money before!

Her mother looked into Tuky's eyes. "You know what to do with this?"

Tuky curtsied and nodded. She had seen exactly how Anyu helped their neighbors before. She kissed her mother's soft hand, and said, "*Kis di hant, Anyu.*"

She picked up the basket, and off she went – down the stairs, into the courtyard, around the vinegar tree, and onto Kolozsvari Street. Balancing the long basket on her arms, Tuky proudly walked down the street. She felt like one of the big girls now. Imagine what Bozi would say if he knew she had twenty pengö in her pocket!

Arriving at Kohn né's house, Tuky felt a little shy. She took a deep breath and knocked on the door. It took a few minutes until a thin young woman appeared. Tuky's heart was beating in her ears, and she couldn't hear her own voice at first.

"Good afternoon, Kohn né. My mother sent…"

"Tuky! Bless your dear mother. Come in, child."

Tuky was glad she didn't have to say too

much more. She did exactly as Anyu had instructed her and unpacked the heavy basket. There was no other food in the house except some stale bread on the cutting board.

After Kohn né went off to rest, Tuky took the new baby into her arms. He was light and small, but not very easy to hold. He wiggled and fussed, shaking his head from side to side. Tuky held on tightly, not wanting to wake up Kohn né.

"Oh, what would Anyu do?" thought Tuky. "Will she be sorry she sent me instead of Hindi or Mirca?"

Suddenly, Tuky remembered a little song her mother sang to Miki at night. It couldn't hurt to try.

"*Hei li, lu, lu, lu,*" she sang softly. The baby looked at her. Tuky sang louder and rocked him in her arms.

She sat cuddling the baby until he grew calm and quiet. His eyes drooped, and he snuggled into his blanket. Tuky's arm was stiff by then, but she took special care to hold the baby's head just right.

Tuky let out a deep breath. She had done it!

The baby sighed in his sleep. Tuky stood up and put him into his crib, which was only an empty dresser drawer lined with a blanket. The little apartment was completely quiet, but Tuky had one more job to do. She put her hand into her apron and took out the twenty pengö bill. She glanced around, looking for a good place. Suddenly, Tuky had an idea!

She tiptoed over to the table, and tucked the bill under the tablecloth. Tuky smiled as she imagined the day that Kohn né would find the money and never know how it got there. Anyu always said that giving *tzedoka* this way would keep people from being embarrassed. Tuky took one more look around the simple room, checked on the baby, and slipped out of the house.

On the walk back, carrying the empty basket, Tuky felt wiser and happier than she'd ever felt before.

The sun was low in the sky as she reached home. As Tuky skipped up the steps, she could hear the sounds of her family getting ready for Shabbos. With a great big smile, Tuky ran up to Anyu, "*Kis di hant,* Anyu. I'm back!"

Anyu smiled. "I'm so proud of you."

She held out a fresh honey cookie for a treat. "Eat this, *édes kislány,* then wash up and get dressed. It's almost Shabbos."

Tuky said a *brocha* and took a bite of the soft brown cookie. It was sweet and perfect, like her life, and her wonderful family, and the happiness inside her. Everything was just perfect.

Chapter Four

Tuky hurried to wash up and slip on her beautiful blue Shabbos dress with the gold buttons. It had been made especially for her by Klári the dressmaker. How Tuky loved to stand in front of the oval mirror in the girls' room, twirling and watching her dress fly around her! She swished and curtsied, smiling at herself.

"Stop twirling and come here, Tuky!" Hindi shook her head. "It's getting late!"

Impatiently, her older sister began to brush out Tuky's thick dark hair. When it was sleek and shiny, Hindi parted it neatly in honor of Shabbos.

The two of them made their way down the hall, just in time to help Mirca take Anyu's gold-rimmed china dishes from the cabinet. Then the girls carefully set them on the spotless Shabbos tablecloth.

Everyone helped. Even little Zsuzsa was able to place two *challos* on the *challah* board and cover them with a white embroidered cloth. Anyu placed her silver candlesticks on the table, putting candles in some and olive oil in others.

With everyone helping, napkins, glasses, salt shaker and cutlery seemed to jump into place. By the time they were finished, the table was beautifully set, and Anyu gave her girls a smile and a nod of approval.

The rest of the house was humming with activity. Bujie, the maid, was busy scrubbing the top of the large black cast iron coal oven. When she finished, Anyu opened a small door on the bottom of the oven, adding enough coals to heat the soup and chicken for the night meal. She lit the coals, and when she was sure they were burning properly, Anyu closed the tiny door and placed the soup and chicken on the shiny stove top.

At the same time, Sami and Misu were choosing from a pile of thirty fresh challos cooling in the kitchen. It was their job to pack twenty of Anyu's delicious loaves into a basket, and take them to shul for the next day. They lifted the box and dashed down the stairs in a blink.

Apu called, "Hurry up, children, Anyu is about to light the candles. It is almost Shabbos Kodesh."

All the children came into the front room, as Anyu, wearing an elegant Shabbos dress, was striking the match. She lit the candles and waved her hands over them. Covering her eyes, she said the *brocha*. She stood there, face covered, for quite a few minutes, swaying and davening. All the children stood beside her. Tuky wondered what her Anyu was davening for and thinking about.

"*Gut Shabbos, gut Shabbos,*" said Anyu, lifting her hands from her face.

Each child came up to Anyu and kissed

her hand. Anyu wrapped her arms around each of them in turn. When Anyu held her close, Tuky closed her eyes. It felt so cozy to be in Anyu's warm embrace.

Apu and her brothers were off to shul. Anyu sat down with her *Korban Mincha Siddur.* "Come girls, take your siddurim. Let's daven out loud together. *Lechu neraninah la-Hashem...*"

Every word was pronounced with love. The sing-song of her voice was like music to Tuky's ears. She was glad that she knew how to read from the siddur. Thanks to their tutor, Schiffer Bracha, Tuky and her sisters could follow along with their mother, all together, in the soft glow of the Shabbos candles.

At any time during the week, anyone who needed a meal was always welcome in the Gestetner home. But on Friday night, Tuky loved the way their house would fill with guests. Apu would go to shul with her brothers, and come home with a crowd of poor and lonely people.

One guest always fell asleep in his chair after eating Anyu's chicken with warm and spicy *letcho*. Then there was Aizik the Chazzan, who loved singing *zemiros* with Apu, but always sang off key. Another guest was Tachsheit the Fishman, who always ate two portions of Anyu's fish. In addition to the regulars, there was usually someone new.

When the door opened, in came Apu and Tuky's brothers, followed by the Shabbos guests. One of them was a tall, skinny young man they had never seen before. Tuky wondered why his coat was creased and his shoes looked so worn and dusty. His head was bent, and when he looked up, his eyes were the saddest that Tuky had ever seen.

Apu said, *"Gut Shabbos, Anyu. Gut Shabbos,* my beautiful children. Tonight we have a new guest. His name is Tzvi, and he is from Austria."

"Shalom Aleichem..." sang Apu. The guests joined in with him. When they finished, the children lined up in front of Apu. He

looked at Hindi, put his hands on her head, and *bentched* her. Then, Hindi went to kiss Anyu's hand and sit down in her place. One by one, from oldest to youngest, Apu

bentched his sons and daughters. Then they went over to kiss their mother's hand.

From her corner at the end of the table, Tuky loved to gaze at her father, so strong and

tall, dressed in his Shabbos suit. She loved everything about Apu, from the way his steady hand poured wine into his silver *becher*, to the flash of his gold tooth as he recited the Kiddush. Everyone answered "Amein," and then stood to wash at the corner sink.

When they had all washed and dried their hands, Apu raised two of Anyu's finest challos, and said the *brocha* out loud. He cut a piece of the crisp *challah*, dipped it into salt, and took a small bite. He then distributed *challah* to Anyu, the guests, and the children.

Anyu brought out a platter of fish. She served the sliced fish in sauce to Apu and to all those seated around the table. After everyone enjoyed the first course and had a drink, Anyu brought out the steaming chicken soup. The golden broth, spiced with ginger, had carrots floating on top. Black skinned radishes, peeled, sliced and artfully set on a plate, were passed around to crunch with the soup. Everyone loved Anyu's food, but Tuky couldn't help noticing that Tzvi, the new guest, was eating as if he had hadn't seen food in a long time.

When Misu banged his chair by mistake, Tzvi jumped at the sound. Whenever Hindi or Mirca came to serve behind him, Tzvi turned his head with a fearful look. Tuky watched the new guest thoughtfully. What was the matter with him? What could have made him so afraid?

After singing *zemiros* and *bentching*, Tzvi remained at the table with Apu. Tuky and her sisters cleared the table, and brought all the dishes to the kitchen to wash. Tuky, still curious, came back to the table and slowly wiped off the *challah* crumbs, trying to hear Apu and Tzvi's conversation.

"I've been going from place to place, Gestetner úr. The German soldiers, the Nazis, are taking over every country they can."

Tuky was confused. What were German soldiers doing in other places? Couldn't they stay in their own country and protect their own people? It must have something to do with the war.

"We used to live in a big house, and my father had a hardware store.

Then, when all the Jews were forced to move into a ghetto neighborhood, we were crammed into a small apartment with another few families."

Tuky was shocked. How terrible! Her heart went out to poor Tzvi, living in such a crowded way. She tried to imagine her whole family all sleeping in one room, but how? Would they sleep on chairs or on the floor?

Tzvi lowered his voice. There were tears in his eyes. Tuky had to lean forward to hear what he said next.

"There wasn't enough food or heat. People were getting sick and couldn't get medicine. I tried to eat less and give my share to my little brothers…"

Now Tuky understood why Tzvi looked so scared and ate so quickly. He really was frightened. He knew what it meant to be hungry. She felt like crying for the poor families and children in Austria.

Suddenly, Apu looked up and saw Tuky standing with her hand full of *challah* crumbs. Her face looked pale and frightened.

Apu shook his head. "Into bed, *édes kislány*. Good Shabbos."

"Good Shabbos," Tuky whispered. She walked slowly from the room, Tzvi's voice following her down the hallway.

"Listen to me, Gestetner úr! It's not safe anymore for a Jew to live under German control. Soon it's not going to be safe here in Budapest. The Nazis are heading to Hungary. You should try to leave. Go somewhere safe before it's too late!"

Tuky said *Shema*, but lay awake in her bed for a long time that night. Questions filled her mind. Was Tzvi right? Were the Nazi soldiers going to come to their beautiful city? Would her family have to leave Hungary? Would everyone have to sleep in one room and not have enough to eat? Tuky shivered.

A sudden thought came to her.

"We are all in *Hashem Yisborach's* Hands." That's what Anyu often said. And her Anyu was always right. With that, Tuky rolled over and went to sleep.

Chapter Five

For Tuky, nothing was quite the same after that Shabbos.

Of course she still worked on her handkerchief each day, finishing all the yellow flowers and starting on the blue ones. Of course she still stood on her head to enjoy the upside down view, played with her cousins, and rode her bike faster than ever. But as the weeks passed, more and more people started coming to Budapest. Their troubled faces reminded Tuky of Tzvi from Austria.

These men, women and children came from many different countries. There were some from Poland, and some from Czechoslovakia. All were trying to get away from the Nazi soldiers. All were looking for a place to stay and something to eat.

Hindi told her that they were called refugees, since they had to run away for refuge, a place of safety. Of course, they were welcome at Tuky's house, and the whole Gestetner family tried to make them feel at home.

That winter, Anyu and Apu were constantly busy with all the guests. Since their

house was on top of Apu's fabric factory, they were able to keep many people safe and warm. When the beds upstairs were full, Apu and his brother, Colev bácsi, would go down to the factory, unroll bolts of fabric, and let people sleep on the soft material. In the morning, they would roll up the fabric once again, and come upstairs to join the family for their meals.

One night, as Apu was unrolling a bolt of fabric for yet another refugee, he said, "We are the only family who can give each guest a brand new bed!"

Many times, Tuky would fall asleep in her bed, and in the morning, she would wake up on some fabric on the floor. She would peek up at her own bed to see who had arrived the night before. It was always someone who needed a real bed more than she did.

She felt so happy to still be in her own comfortable home with plenty of food. Yet Tuky just couldn't help but wonder, "Will life ever get back to the way it was?"

And every time she wondered, it seemed that things would change even more.

That spring, the German army marched in and took control of Hungary. When Tuky looked out of the window one morning, she saw two Nazi soldiers in their brown uniforms. Their tall boots crunched in the gravel as they made their way down Kolozsvari Street, past the budding branches of the vinegar tree. Tuky knew the soldiers couldn't see her, but she ducked behind the table anyway, just in case. She wished they would go away, like a bad dream.

Then there was the day, right before Pesach, that Anyu sat at the dining room table, cutting yellow felt into stars, and sewing them on everyone's jackets and coats.

"But why, Anyu?" Tuky had asked. "My new spring jacket looks so much nicer the way it is."

"It's a new law, a German law," Anyu answered. "They're in charge now, and they want to see exactly who is Jewish."

Tuky just couldn't understand. Why would a big country like Germany care if a little girl in Hungary was Jewish, and what she wore on her jacket? Life was changing in ways that Tuky didn't like.

One day, when he came home, Apu called the whole family together. "I have something for you," he said.

Tuky was so curious! She loved gifts. What would it be?

Apu took a roll of one pengö coins from his pocket. He held it up and explained.

"Your Colev bácsi and I found out where the Belzer Rebbe is hiding from the Germans. We went to see the *tzaddik* and asked him to *bentch* these coins. The Rebbe put his hands on them, closed his eyes, and said that with Hashem's help, the wearers of these coins will remain safe. I've had a hole drilled in each one so you can keep it with you always."

Carefully, Apu strung each coin on a chain. "We will wear these around our necks."

"Even the boys?" asked Misu.

"Yes, even the boys. These are not ordinary coins anymore. With Hashem's help, the *brocha* of the *tzaddik* will protect us."

The children gathered around Apu. His face was very serious. He looked each child in the eye and put a silver chain with the blessed coin around their necks. When it was Tuky's turn, he hugged her close.

The cold metal of the coin grew warm against Tuky's skin. It made her feel special and safe. As the days went by, she became used to the weight of it around her neck. The yellow star was only on her jacket, but her father's coin with the *tzaddik's brocha* was right next to her heart.

Chapter Six

War, war, war. All through the spring and summer, it seemed to be the only thing everyone talked about. Tuky was a little girl, but she was old enough to worry. She no longer rushed down to play with the others in the courtyard. Tuky preferred to stay on the large porch upstairs where she could hear her mother cooking in the kitchen. Nestled on the porch, she felt safe from all her scary thoughts.

It was also the best place to watch the vinegar tree change its colors when fall came. Tuky loved the sight of the brilliant red leaves, swaying in the autumn wind. Up on the porch, she could pretend everything was fine.

Then one day, a day she would never forget, there was loud banging at the door. Anyu opened it, and there stood two German soldiers, stiff and unsmiling.

"We are here to speak to Gestetner né," they announced.

Anyu straightened her shoulders. "I am Gestetner né," she answered quietly.

"Where is your husband?"

"He is out now," replied Anyu. Apu had gone to shul that morning and had not yet returned.

One soldier held out some papers. "Never mind your husband. We found his brother in the factory. You must both come with us to headquarters," he said.

Stepping back in shock Anyu asked, "What is this all about?"

The officer narrowed his eyes. "You will find out at headquarters. You Jews are always asking questions. Now, gather all your children and bring them along with you."

"Surely you don't need to arrest the children! This cannot be!" exclaimed Anyu.

"Hurry!" ordered the soldier. "The truck is waiting below!"

Anyu gathered her frightened family. She made sure that all the children added a few layers of underclothing to what they wore. Then she had the girls layer one dress over another, and the boys put on a few pairs of pants and shirts.

"We don't know how long we will be away from home," she said. "May Hashem protect us!"

As Tuky pulled a skirt on over her dress, she had a million questions. It all had to be a silly mistake. Why did soldiers need little children? They were too young to help with the war. And where was Apu? Surely Apu would tell them they were at the wrong house, taking the wrong people.

One guard walked in front with Colev bácsi, followed by Anyu, holding Miki in her arms. Tuky began marching down the steps behind her mother, holding tightly to Zsuzsa's hand. Sami and Misu came next. Mirca picked up Frédi and carried him outside. Hindi was the last one out the door. She paused and took a long look at the mezuzah on the doorpost.

Tuky knew just what she was thinking. *We're all in Hashem's Hands.*

For once, the children were quiet. As young as they were, they understood the danger that faced them. Tuky thought she would try to sneak away to find Apu, but when she saw the officer's menacing look, she quickly changed her mind.

With pounding hearts, the family walked outside the gates behind the officers. Waiting for them on Kolozsvari Street was a military truck. Roughly, the soldiers ordered them into the back of the military truck.

"Hurry, hurry!" said the soldiers. "We don't have all day!"

Tuky felt like crying. She swallowed and blinked to keep the tears back. How dare these guards talk to her mother and her uncle this way?

With the soldiers shouting, they all scrambled up into the truck and sat down.

Tuky found a spot on the splintery wooden bench and leaned against Hindi. Anyu sat upright, dignified as always, cradling Miki in her arms.

"Now we're going for a little ride," she said. "I need you to behave and do as you are told. All this will be straightened out very soon."

The truck started moving. Everyone jerked from the sudden movement. Zsuzsa began to whimper. As they turned the corner, Tuky saw a familiar shape across the street. Could it be her Apu? She wanted to wave or call out to him, but she thought it wouldn't be a good idea. Just then, he turned around and walked into an apartment building. *Where was he going? Why didn't he come over and save them?*

Peering out from her spot, Tuky watched people walking in the street. They stared when they saw a truck full of children. Tuky wondered what they were thinking. Did they feel sorry for her?

Bumping and turning, stopping and starting, the truck made its way toward a part of town far away from Kolozsvari Street. The smoke from the exhaust and the awful smell of gasoline made Tuky dizzy and sick. When would the truck stop? When could they all get off?

Just as Tuky thought she couldn't take any more, the truck came to a sudden stop in front of an imposing grey building. The building's small windows were covered with bars. There was a sign above the large black door at the entrance that read: Rokszilard Street Prison.

Tuky whispered to Anyu, "Why are we here? Isn't a prison for robbers?"

Holding her head up high, Anyu said, "No one thinks we are robbers. We are here for one reason. There are people who don't like us because we are Jews, and they are trying to make trouble for us."

A guard came around to the back of the truck. "Everyone off!" he barked. "Follow the other officer into the building."

As Anyu stood up and straightened her skirt, she turned to Tuky and to all her children, "Be proud of who you are. Be proud to be a Jew. Remember, we are all in Hashem's Hands."

Tuky was too scared to cry. Her stomach felt like she'd swallowed a lot of stones. She jumped off the truck and helped Zsuzsa get down. The family was led into the large building. What would happen inside? What would become of them now?

The soldier in charge called out, "Gestetner né, Gestetner úr, this way for questioning."

Anyu quickly handed Miki to Hindi. "Do exactly what they tell you," she instructed, "and take care of Miki and the little ones!"

The children watched as their uncle and their mother were led down a long hallway and disappeared around the corner. No one seemed to care what the children did, so Hindi sat them down on some wooden benches.

"Not a sound," she ordered. "We will wait here for Anyu to come back."

The bewildered children waited and waited. Scared and hungry, they dared not make a sound. One minute dragged into another. Zsuzsa and Miki fell asleep. Frédi fussed and whined. Where was everyone?

Tuky grew restless. She counted the bars on the windows. She kicked her feet back and forth. She unlaced her shoes, laced them back up, and tied them tightly. If she had to walk back home, at least she'd be ready!

Over and over, Tuky wondered, "Where is Apu right now? When is he coming to take us home?"

🌷 🌷 🌷

Hours passed. People came and went, officers marched back and forth, but no one even glanced at the children.

Tuky sighed and shifted on the hard wooden bench. It felt as though they'd been sitting there for days!

Finally, when it was almost evening, two women arrived, dressed in grey woolen coats. The younger one had a red and blue kerchief tied under her chin. The older one wore a black kerchief tied in the same way. They looked at the sleepy children with pity in their eyes.

The women spoke to the soldier in charge. He pulled out a large stack of papers and slapped them on the desk.

"After these are signed, the children are all yours," laughed the officer. "You'll have your hands full!"

As the older woman signed the papers one at a time, the children waited, holding their breath. The younger lady turned to them, and said, "You must all be very good and come with us. We are taking you to safety."

Hindi turned to her little brothers and sisters. "Anyu told us to do exactly as we are told, remember?"

They nodded. None of them wanted to spend even one extra minute in jail.

Helping each other up, the children followed the women out of the building and into two waiting taxis. Tuky got in with Misu and Sami. The older lady with the black kerchief got in after them and told the driver where to go. Tuky looked surprised. *Why weren't they going home to Kolozsvari Street? Was this some kind of mistake?*

As the taxi sped down the street, the woman tried to explain everything to Tuky and her brothers.

"It's not safe to go back to your house. We have friends and neighbors who have agreed to take you for a few days. Not all of you together, you understand."

The taxi pulled up and stopped at an unfamiliar corner.

"Here we are. Which one of you is Tuky?"

Anxiously, Tuky lifted her hand. Her throat was dry. She couldn't swallow.

"You get out here. You will stay with Anna."

The door of the taxi opened to reveal an older woman with kind blue eyes, a wrinkled face, and a white bun at the nape of her neck.

She held out her hand to the scared little girl.

"I am Anna."

Tuky gulped as she got out of the taxi. The sun had long gone down. And the moon, only a silver sliver, seemed to peek from behind the large building. She turned to blow a kiss to her family in the taxi. She watched as they drove off into the night, turned a corner, and couldn't be seen anymore.

Tuky looked down at her shoes as she walked with Anna into an old apartment building. It smelled of cabbage and onions. Tuky was so tired that she could barely climb the stairs to the second floor.

Anna unlocked the door, and they both walked into the small apartment. By the dim light of a floor lamp, Tuky could see the front room with two brown armchairs. The curtains were drawn, and the lamplight cast long, dark shadows on the ceiling.

Tuky sagged against the wall. Her awful day in jail was over, but what would tomorrow bring? As the door closed, big hot tears streamed down Tuky's face. She blinked and sniffed, trying to hide that she was crying.

"Come in, pretty one," said Anna. "I'll take care of you for the next few days. You will be safe here."

Tuky knew that a six-year-old girl should be brave, but she couldn't hold back her tears. It seemed as if they would never stop.

Tuky cried for her mother. *Was she still in jail?* She cried for her brothers and sisters. *Where were they now?* She cried for her father. *When would he come to get her?*

She cried as she nibbled at some food. She cried when she got into bed that night. Before she fell asleep, Tuky clutched her necklace with the blessed coin from the Belzer Rebbe and cried some more. She cried and cried for a day and a half. Nothing Anna said or did could stop the river of tears from falling.

Finally, Anna told her, "Tuky, if you wash your face, and dry your tears, we're going out. I have a great surprise for you."

Tuky was curious. She washed her face, just as Anna had instructed her to. Peering at Anna through swollen eyes, Tuky waited to hear what her surprise would be.

Chapter Seven

Tuky held Anna's hand tightly as they left the tiny apartment.

Stepping into the morning sunlight, Tuky squinted. What a contrast this was to Anna's dark rooms! Maybe, just maybe, everything would change now. Maybe she'd be able to go back home to her family. Looking from side to side, Tuky hoped to find her Apu waiting for her. How she longed to run into his arms!

Anna and Tuky walked down the block, and around the corner. A few minutes later, a large black car pulled up next to them. Anna said, "Tuky, listen to me. You go into that car, with the kind Schober né and her husband."

Tuky stopped walking and asked, "Who?"

Anna said, "They are friends. Your parents sent them to pick you up. Get in quickly, so people won't stare at us."

Tuky did as she was told. As she settled herself on the large leather seat, Anna quickly closed the door. Tuky looked out the window as the car started moving. She waved to Anna.

The lady sitting next to the driver turned and said, "My name is Schober né. I met your aunt, Terus néni on the tram one day. My husband and I are good Hungarian citizens who hate what the Nazis are doing. Now I am trying to help your parents keep you safe."

Tuky studied the kind woman's face. Schober né looked just like any other Hungarian woman. The little girl couldn't believe that someone who just met her aunt would be willing to help them. It felt like a miracle.

The car turned onto a small street, and pulled up in front of a plain white house. "Here we are," said Schober né.

She led Tuky around the back of the

house, and the two of them stepped inside. As the door closed, Tuky looked around. Sitting at the table was her Apu! Although he seemed tired, he looked up and smiled at her, his gold tooth winking happily.

Apu got up and Tuky ran towards him. She fell into his open arms, hugging him tightly, as if she'd never let go. For the first time in days, the tight knot in Tuky's chest relaxed.

Suddenly she noticed two peasant boys standing behind Apu. They looked like farmer's children, dressed in shabby faded shirts, with caps pulled down over their foreheads.

"Hi, Tuky," said one. Tuky stared and laughed. It was her cousin, Puncsi. The second boy turned round. It was her very own brother, Misu! *How funny the boys looked! Why were they wearing those farm clothes?*

Tuky glanced at her father, but he seemed very serious. Apu gathered the children around the table, and began talking in a low voice.

"Children, *Boruch Hashem*, Anyu and Colev bácsi have both been released from jail. I don't want you to worry about them."

He took a deep breath. "But Budapest, and all of Hungary, has become a very dangerous place for Jews. The Nazi soldiers are gathering every Jew they can find and... sending them far away. They blame the Jews for everything that goes wrong. The law is: no Jews allowed."

Apu shook his head. "Now, my dear children, these good people will help you hide so that the Nazis don't find you."

Apu sighed, and continued, "Schober né has some friends in a small farm town, out in the country. It is about a two hour ride from Budapest. The name of the town is Cibakháza. The Ladics Family and a few other farmers will help us."

Tuky looked at her father in shock. *Could they really go and live on a farm?*

Would they have to milk cows? Tuky didn't know anything about farms or animals. Her family had always lived in their comfortable home above the factory.

Her father continued, "It is very important for you to remember not to let anyone guess that you are Jewish. You will have to be careful all the time."

Schober né appeared in the doorway. In her hand was a small pile of creased clothing. "Come here, child. I have a dress, apron and jacket for you to wear."

Tuky wrinkled her nose at the sorry-looking outfit.

Apu said, "I know that this clothing is different than yours, but it is very important that you fit in. Go along with Schober né and change."

Tuky took off her jacket with the yellow star. She shed her own lovely dresses and skirts and hung them on the back of a chair. With a sigh, she pulled the stiff peasant dress over her head and fastened the buttons.

Schober né tied the wrinkled apron around Tuky's waist. How different it was from her own blue and white one that she loved! When she came out of the room in the strange rough clothing, Tuky did not feel like herself at all. Glancing at her reflection in a mirror, she was almost surprised to see that her face looked the same.

There was a sharp knock, and then three quick knocks, and then two knocks. As she opened the door, Schober né reassured them. "Don't worry, it's safe. This must be Ladics úr."

At the door stood a tall man with a large, red face. His overalls were worn, but clean. He said simply, "I've come for the children."

Apu stood up, and went to greet the newcomer. Reaching into his pocket, Apu removed a small sack and handed it to the farmer. Eagerly, Ladics úr counted the coins inside.

"This seems enough for now. But if we have to hide them for longer..."

Apu said, "There will be more, if necessary. Thank you."

That's when Tuky really understood. Apu and Anyu wouldn't be going with them. The farmer was being paid to hide Puncsi, Misu, and herself. With wide eyes, Tuky looked up at the Hungarian farmer. She felt like gluing herself to her chair.

Apu could barely speak. "Tuky, come here."

She looked up at Apu, trying to memorize his face. His dark brown eyes were shut tightly, and his usually cheerful face was now very serious. She wanted him to smile, so she could see his gold tooth, but Apu was crying.

He put his hands on her head and gave her a *brocha*. He hugged her tightly and whispered into her ear, "Remember that you are a Jewish girl. Remember that your name is Malka."

Of course she would remember; she knew what her real name was. Again and again, he repeated this to her.

Afterwards, Apu gave a *brocha* to the two boys. Then there was one last hug for her.

Tuky held the little boys' hands and helped them into the farmer's wagon. Puncsi

was six, and Misu was only five. If she cried, they would cry, too! Even though Tuky's heart was beating fast, her eyes stayed dry. It was as if she'd used up all her tears during her lonely time at Anna's house.

The boys loved the fun of riding in the bumpy wagon. They enjoyed watching the powerful horse clip-clop down the road. Only Tuky remained deep in thought.

Leaning close to Misu and Puncsi, she whispered, "In front of the farmers of Cibakháza, we will have to act just like everyone else. But remember; no matter what happens, we are really Jewish inside."

Misu looked at her and said, "When can we go home?"

"*Hashem Yisborach* will help, and the war will end. Then we will be able to go home," she said, patting him on the hand.

As they neared the little farm town, Ladics úr turned to the children and said: "You, girl! Your name will now be Ladics, Mária. Repeat it to me!"

Tuky swallowed hard, and repeated her false new name in a shaky voice, "Loh-ditch Mah-ria."

"Louder," he demanded.

"Loh-ditch Mah-ria!"

"We have the same last name now, and you will call me uncle while you stay in my house."

Tuky swallowed. "Yes, Ladics bácsi."

"It's very important that you never tell anyone who you are. Your brother and your cousin better remember their new names, too. The big one will be Andris, and the small one, Miska. They'll live at a farm nearby."

Then, turning to the boys, he ordered, "Repeat your names, just the way Mária did!"

Hesitantly, the boys tried out their new names.

"An-drash," said Puncsi.

"Mish-ka," chanted Misu.

The farmer's face relaxed. He didn't look quite as huge and harsh as before.

"Remember that I am doing you a very big favor. If you make one small mistake, someone might find out who you are. That would be extremely dangerous..."

Tuky nodded. She understood all too well. Putting her arms around the two little boys, she knew she had to be the big one now, the one in charge.

Chapter Eight

"Well, here we are!" said Ladics bácsi. He pulled back on the reins, and the horses came to a stop in front of a small, run down farmhouse. A tired-looking woman was churning butter on the front porch.

Ladics bácsi called out, "Look what I brought for you, neighbor!"

The woman shook her head and answered, "A few more mouths to feed, I suppose."

Tuky motioned to Puncsi – no, he was Andris now – that he had to get out.

"This is your new home," Tuky whispered. "Try not to make trouble!"

Puncsi-Andris looked scared, but he jumped down from the wagon without a fuss.

Ladics bácsi reached into the sack and handed the woman a few coins. It just reminded Tuky that all these families were hiding them for pay. They had to be very careful. Even in her mind, Tuky decided to think of the boys only with their new names.

She turned to little Miska.

"You're next," she said. "You have to be brave like Andris!"

"I will, Mária," he said, puffing up his chest. "I'm very big and very brave."

With her thick, powerful arms, the woman swung the little boy down from the wagon. As the horses starting moving again, Tuky tried not to look back. It hurt her heart to see the boys walking away with someone else. She wished they could all live under one roof.

As they clip-clopped up the road, Tuky tried to prepare herself. *What would the Ladics Family be like? Would they be kind?*

Tuky decided to be as quiet as she

could, and not to ask for anything. Maybe then, they'd be glad to have her.

The horses stopped in front of a one story house with a bench in the front. Tuky jumped down from the wagon, her legs feeling a little unsteady as she walked toward the house.

Playing in the yard were two girls with long blonde braids. They looked up as the newcomer approached, inspecting her curiously.

Ladics bácsi announced, "Girls, this is my cousin's daughter from Budapest. Her name is Mária, and she's come to stay for a while."

"*Szervusz*, Mária," the girls chanted.

Tuky felt shy, but she smiled at the blonde sisters. She loved the way their yellow hair glinted in the sun. Her own short, dark hair seemed so plain in comparison.

All three girls walked inside the dark farmhouse. Tuky couldn't believe it! The floor was made of earth. There was a rough wooden table with benches on each side. Ladics néni, the woman of the house, stood facing the doorway. Her round face was framed by a colorful scarf, and she wore a long pleated black skirt edged with colorful ribbon. A work apron was tied tightly around her waist.

The farmer's wife looked Tuky up and down without saying a word. Tuky stared back. She felt very uncomfortable.

"What's your name?" the woman asked.

"Mária," answered Tuky. The woman nodded, but did not smile. "My girls are Rószi and Kata. You do whatever they do."

When Ladics bácsi came in from the barn, they all sat down at the table. Ladics néni gave each of them some bread and a bowl of soup. Tuky copied the girls' every move, from the way they drank the soup straight from the bowl, to the way they wiped their mouth on their sleeves. She knew she had to look as if she were part of the family.

Ladics néni's blue eyes were always watching.

"Time for bed, girls," said Ladics úr.

"But where will Mária sleep?" asked Rószi.

"With the two of you," answered their father. "Go on, now."

Tuky followed the girls into a small, dark room. In the corner, was a lumpy straw mattress covered with feed sacks. A faded woolen blanket lay on top.

"This must be the bed," Tuky thought. It looked nothing like her comfortable bed at home, with its starched white linen.

"I call the middle," said Kata. "It's warmer there."

Rószi, the taller of the two, shook her head. "You're such a baby. Fine. You can sleep in between Mária and me. You don't mind, do you, Mária?"

Tuky felt so shy. She was grateful to be asked. "Of course I don't mind. It's your house and your bed."

Kata looked at Tuky thoughtfully. "How old are you, Mária?"

Tuky drew herself up to her full height. "I'm six and a half."

"How come we didn't see you and your family when we went to Budapest last winter? We saw so many other cousins, aunts, and uncles at holiday time!"

Tuky thought fast. "We went on a trip last winter. My mother was sorry to miss your visit, but my father said it couldn't be helped. Anyway, how old are you?"

"I'm nine," Katya said proudly, "and Rószi is ten. We know how to embroider lots of fancy stitches, and I'm putting lots of flowers on my best Sunday skirt!"

Tuky looked impressed. "I just learned how to embroider. Back home, I'm working on a handkerchief with flowers!"

"I'll show you my skirt tomorrow," Kata said. "I bet it's much fancier than anything you can do."

"Maybe," said Tuky. "But can you do this?"

She bent over, kicked her feet upward, and stood on her head in fine fashion!

Kata scowled, but Rószi clapped her hands and said, "Good for you, Mária! That will show Kata to keep her bragging to herself."

Tuky stood back up, her face flushed and eager. She turned to Kata and held out her hand.

"You can help me with my sewing, and I'd be glad to teach you how to stand on your head."

"It's a deal," said Kata. "Let's start now!"

The girls tried to be quiet, but practicing a headstand means lots of funny flops and bumps! There was some giggling and a little teasing before a stern warning came from outside the door.

"Quiet, girls!" said Ladics bácsi.

The three of them jumped up, and quickly continued getting ready for sleep. Kata and Rószi took off their aprons and dresses, laying them neatly on a small bench in the corner. They stopped by the side of the bed, closed their eyes, and bent their heads in prayer.

"Do whatever they do," Tuky thought to herself.

She bent her head, closed her eyes, and whispered the *Shema*.

The two sisters settled themselves under the quilt and motioned for Tuky to join them.

As she tried to find a comfortable spot on the lumpy mattress, Tuky realized how tired she felt. But sleep would not come. The straw poked her in the back, and the woolen blanket felt scratchy and rough.

She closed her eyes, pretending to be asleep.

"She really is good at standing on her head," whispered Kata, "but soon I'll be even better!"

"Mmmmm," Rószi answered in a drowsy voice, but Kata kept talking.

"I can't figure out why Father agreed to have our cousin stay. I thought that the war made everything so expensive!"

"Hush," Rószi answered. "She might hear you! I think her parents are paying good money so she can stay out of the city during war time. It's safer here in the country."

"The neighbors have two city boys," Kata said. "My friend told me."

"You see," Rószi said. "We're not the only ones who have to share our house and our food."

"Well, she's taking up too much room in the bed," Kata complained. "This war is stupid."

"It is," Rószi agreed. "It's a stupid war because of stupid Jews."

Little by little, Tuky rolled sideways to leave more room for the Ladics girls. She lay very still, waiting for them to fall asleep. She knew that Jews were not stupid. She knew that the war was not because of the Jews.

But they think so. Probably all the people in Cibakháza think so. And they must never find out I am Jewish.

As soon as their breathing became slow and steady, Tuky reached for the silver coin around her neck. She pictured her parents' faces, and it was as if she could hear their words in her mind, "Do as you are told... Take care of the little ones...Remember you are a Jewish girl... Remember your name is Malka... We are all in Hashem's Hands..."

Before she knew it, Tuky was fast asleep.

🌱 🌱 🌱

It was pitch black when a loud, unfamiliar sound cut through the air. Tuky sat bolt upright in the lumpy bed and clutched Kata's arm in fright.

"What's that?" she whispered.

Kata didn't even open her eyes. "Rooster," she mumbled. "Time to get up."

Rooster? Tuky said *Modeh Ani* and lay back down. This was country life, and it was very different than anything she knew about.

The girls got up and dressed, then made their way into the kitchen. A big pot of *griz* was bubbling on the stovetop, making Tuky's mouth water. When she got her bowl of *griz* and milk, she thought about how Anyu always made lovely designs with cocoa on top of the *griz* back home.

Tuky sighed, made a secret *brocha*, and dutifully finished the whole bowl.

"What's next?" she asked Kata and Rószi. "Do we have to milk cows or plant crops?"

The sisters laughed at their city "cousin's" question.

"Of course not!" Kata giggled. "Father plants the crops, and our farmhand, Miklós, milks the cows. I help Rószi feed the chickens and gather the eggs, but Mother would never trust you. You can watch."

The girls went outside in the chilly morning air. Tuky took a deep breath, and skipped along behind Kata and Rószi. The girls let her throw a few handfuls of grain on the ground outside the hen house. It was fun to see the hungry chickens peck at their breakfast! Then the farm girls carefully filled two large baskets with eggs and brought them inside.

They emerged from the house a few moments later, with big smiles on their faces. "Let's hike through the fields and visit our neighbors," said Rószi.

"Maybe we'll meet those two city boys," added Kata. "We can have races or play in the barn."

Tuky's heart swelled. She would get to see Miska and Andris!

"Let's go!" she said.

The sky was a beautiful blue, dotted with white, puffy clouds. Tuky couldn't believe how much sky there was, here in the country. She lagged behind Rószi and

Kata, using the time to daven without them noticing.

Before long, they arrived at the neighboring farmhouse, and Miska and Andris were right there on the porch.

"Miska! Andris!" she called. Tuky hoped they would remember that she was Mária now.

"Mária!" they said, running toward her.

"I know these boys," she explained to Rószi and Kata. "They lived right near me in Budapest."

"Let's all go to the stream and collect rocks," Kata said. "Or maybe we can catch a fish."

The children ran off together, and Tuky was relieved. No one knew they were Jews. All they had to do was keep anyone from ever finding out.

🌱 🌱 🌱

In the country, one day was much like the next. After tidying their room, eating breakfast, and gathering eggs, the girls were free to play in the fields. They ran and hiked with the neighbor's children, and Tuky was grateful that she could see the boys very often. Together, they collected rocks, picked wildflowers, and climbed fences.

And of course, the girls practiced their headstands and their sewing indoors on rainy days.

Once a week, Rozsi, Kata, and Tuky sprinkled water on the earthern floor of the house and swept it with a stiff straw broom.

At noontime each day, the sound of the drummer beckoned the people to the town square. There, after a long drum roll, the town crier would announce the latest news. All the farmers, their wives, and even the children would gather around to hear about the war.

Most of the time, the news was bad, and generally, the townspeople blamed the Jews.

"It's the Jews' fault we can't get more supplies."

"If not for those Jews, the war would be over!"

"I don't know how the Jews manage to make so much trouble."

Andris would look down and clench his fists when he heard such talk. But Tuky poked him with her elbow. "Act like you don't care," she always said.

These country people accepted the three city children as the Ladics Family's relatives from Budapest. They had no clue that they were really Jewish children hiding from the Nazis. If they would have known, they would not have allowed Tuky and the boys to remain in their town for even one moment.

Tuky never forgot that she was in charge. She tried to keep a watchful eye on her cousin and her brother. She would daven while walking on the country roads, where no one could hear her. She taught the boys to do the same.

Of all days, Shabbos was the hardest for Tuky. It was then that she missed her family the most. Tuky closed her eyes and tried to picture her house on Shabbos: the glowing Shabbos candles, the table full of guests. She sometimes pretended she was eating Anyu's delicious *challah*, the soup with crunchy radishes, or the hearty cholent with meat.

Shabbos on the farm was nothing like this. Tuky always made sure to find a reason why she couldn't sew on long Shabbos afternoons. "I hurt my finger on a sharp thorn," she'd say to Kata, or "That stitch is too hard for me. I'll just watch you and Rószi embroider."

One sunny morning in the spring, Ladics bácsi came in for breakfast looking tired but happy.

"Neighbor's cow had a calf last night," he announced. "She's a beauty!"

Kata and Rozsi squealed with excitement. "Which neighbor? Can we go and see it?"

Their father nodded. "János bácsi's farm, right down the road. Give the new mother some time to rest, and you can visit this afternoon."

Tuky had never seen a newborn calf. Today would be fun!

They did their daily chores, and soon it was time to go.

"Let's stop by for Andris and Miska," said Kata. "They probably want to see the darling little calf, too!"

So, the girls hiked over, and the boys joined them for the walk to the neighbor's farm.

Inside a small fenced-in area, the mother cow was licking the small calf that leaned against her. The calf's shiny brown eyes were soft and sweet. The city children were totally fascinated with the animal, charmed by its attempt to walk on skinny, wobbly legs.

János bácsi approached, and the children greeted him.

"How do you like her?" he asked, pointing at the healthy new calf.

"She's precious!" answered Kata. Tuky couldn't take her eyes off the cow and her baby, but little Miska was even more enraptured.

"May I have her?" begged the little boy. "I never had a pet before."

János bácsi smiled.

"You can't take a calf away from her mother until she's a few months old. She's got to grow a bit."

Miska's eyes glowed with excitement. *In a few months, he would own that calf!*

Every day after that, the children returned to check up on the little animal. They saw her filling out and growing stronger. Tuky reached between the fence rails to pat her softly.

"Is she two months old yet?" asked Miska.

"Almost," his sister answered. "Why?"

"Because that's when János bácsi said I could have her," said the little boy.

Tuky smiled and turned away. She knew Miska had misunderstood. János bácsi wasn't about to give a valuable calf to a little boy like him.

"Well," thought Tuky to herself, "Miska will find out he's not getting that calf soon enough. Why should I tell him now? It won't make any difference."

Little did she know what a very big difference it would make!

Chapter Nine

The very next day in the town square, Andris and Miska went looking for János bácsi. The farmer was discussing the latest news of the war with Ladics bácsi and two other men.

Tuky shook her head at the little boys. Now was not the time to bother the grownups.

But Miska was determined. As soon as there was a pause in the conversation, he piped up.

"Good day, János bácsi. Today the little calf is two months old. Can I come and get her now?"

János bácsi looked puzzled. "Get her for what?"

"Get her to keep," answered Miska.

"You said she could leave her mother when she grew a bit."

All the farmers burst into laughter. One of them ruffled Miska's hair and pinched his cheeks.

"Well, son," János bácsi said, "that calf is worth quite a lot of money. She'll be a big strong milk cow one day."

Miska's face looked stricken. "But, you *told* me I could have the calf for a pet."

The men laughed again.

"He's got the makings of a good little farmer," one of them said.

"Not if he expects to get healthy animals for free," said Ladics bácsi.

János bácsi looked kindly at the little boy. "I never meant to give you that calf," he said. "Around here, people buy and sell farm animals, and you have no money. I'm sorry."

Tuky felt upset that she hadn't explained this to the boys before. Miska looked so disappointed. But Andris looked angry.

Before Tuky could stop him, Andris stood as tall as he could and shouted, "When the Russians beat the Germans and my Apu is back in his factory, he can buy that calf. He'll have enough money to buy the whole town of Cibakháza!"

Tuky gasped.

The farmers grew silent.

Ladics bácsi stood stern and unsmiling.

János bácsi turned to him in disbelief. "So, these children, who have a rich father with a factory, are your relatives from Budapest?"

Another farmer spoke up. "Doesn't sound like it to me."

All the men stared at Tuky and the boys.

Tuky stepped behind Kata and Rószi, wishing she could disappear.

János bácsi shook his finger at Ladics bácsi. "They don't look a bit like your family. I always thought they looked like Jews."

"We can't allow them to stay in our

town," said one of the farmers. "We could all be blamed for this!"

Kata and Rószi looked at Tuky as if seeing her for the very first time. Ladics bácsi said nothing. There was nothing to say. Their secret was out!

János bácsi narrowed his eyes. "We're taking them in right now. Who's coming with me?"

Tuky didn't even have a chance to say goodbye to the Ladics sisters. A group of farmers led her and the boys down the road to the nearest headquarters in town.

János bácsi marched the children up to the officer at the front desk. He had blonde hair that was almost white, and a long skinny neck that poked out of his collar. He spoke Hungarian with a thick German accent.

"What's all this?" he asked. "Are these children refusing to eat their vegetables? What have they done wrong?"

János bácsi said quietly, "We think

they're Jewish children from Budapest. We brought them here because that's the law, and we don't want any trouble."

The officer frowned, and his face turned red. "I'll soon get to the bottom of this. You, girl, what's your name?"

Tuky looked him right in the eye and said, "Ladics Mária."

The officer shook his head. "What's your REAL name?"

"Ladics Mária," Tuky said, even louder than before.

"If you're lying, we'll have to put you in jail," shouted the officer.

Tuky just stared at him. She had to act brave in front of the boys.

But the shouting was too much for little Misu. He blurted out, "Don't put her in jail! Her name is Gestetner Malka!"

Tuky sighed and put her arm around her brother. He couldn't help it if he was young and scared and couldn't keep their secret.

"I knew it, you little rascals," said János bácsi. "That's what you get for trying to fool everyone."

The farmers left without looking back. Tuky and the boys huddled together, and she comforted them the best she could.

"Remember the coins we're wearing," she said. "We have a *brocha*, and we'll be just fine. Let's just do what we are told."

"All right, you little Jews," said the officer, "you're in big trouble now."

Grumbling to himself, he rushed the three children out the door. He hopped on his bicycle and ordered, "Follow me!"

As he pedaled, Tuky, Misu and Puncsi ran behind the officer. They had never been so scared in all their lives! Their chests felt like they were on fire from breathing so fast. The wind whipped at their faces and made their eyes tear.

Finally, they arrived at the neighboring town. The officer got off his bike, and took

them to the military outpost. Opening the door wide, he bellowed: "Have I got a catch today! Three Jewish children to give to the Nazis! Who's in charge here?"

"Sorry, sir! You came half a day too late. The German soldiers just left this morning with a truckload full of Jews. Try the next town over. Maybe someone there can take these three off your hands."

Tuky couldn't believe it. They were exhausted, their feet were blistered, and all they wanted to do was sit down and rest. But, when the annoyed officer motioned for them to follow him again, they obeyed.

Thoroughly disgusted, the officer mounted his bike and continued up the same road. Tuky tried not to think, but just to put one foot in front of the other. What a sight! An officer in full uniform riding along, with three little children running behind him, panting and struggling to keep up.

Finally, they arrived at the headquarters in the next town. The desk officer took one look at the strange little group and waved them away. "The soldiers have just cleared out. You've missed them. Try the next town down the road."

But the officer had had enough. "I'm not biking across Hungary with these miserable kids! You can keep them and figure out what to do with them. I have to get back to Cibakháza before dark."

And with that, he marched out!

Chapter Ten

"*Ach*," grumbled the desk officer. He seemed annoyed to be left in charge of these three inconvenient children.

"Come on, then. Quickly! *Schnell!*"

He hurried Tuky and the boys into a small holding cell. It had a tiny window near the ceiling, and a wooden chair in the corner.

"You will stay here for the night, and tomorrow we will decide what to do with you," he muttered.

What about food? Where can we get water? We need blankets! Tuky thought all of these things, but felt too timid to say a word.

"We'll just do as we are told," she thought.

The officer slammed the metal door shut

and locked it.

Tuky looked around and shivered. The cell was cold and damp, with a hard stone floor. They took turns sitting on the chair, then pacing back and forth to keep warm.

When there was no more light coming from the small window, Tuky took charge.

"Time for sleep," she told the boys.

Puncsi and Misu tried to listen, but trying to get comfortable on the floor was impossible.

"Take off your jacket and make a pillow," Tuky told them. Then she sat down next to them and said *Shema*.

"I'll never fall asleep," said Puncsi.

"Me, either," complained Misu.

Tuky knew how they felt. Even the lumpy, crowded mattress in the Ladics's house seemed inviting compared to the floor of the cell.

She lay awake, thinking about how quickly things had changed. First she was a

Jewish girl, living a happy life in the city with a family that did so many mitzvos. Then she was a Jewish girl hiding out in the country, doing mitzvos secretly. Now she was... well, now she was a Jewish girl, just as always. That would never change.

Tuky looked over at the boys. In spite of what they'd said, their eyes were closed, and both were breathing deeply. All that running behind the German officer had tired them out.

As she lay there, tossing and turning, a scary thought came to her. *How will my Apu know where we are? Will he ever be able to find us?*

Tuky's heart ached to be back home with her Apu, Anyu and all her sisters and brothers. But strangely, she didn't cry.

"I'm in charge of the boys," she thought. "I have to be brave. I *will* be brave."

She finally fell asleep, utterly exhausted in the cold, dark cell.

The next thing Tuky knew, light was streaming from the little window, and the officer was banging on the door.

"Up, up! Come on, wake up! Today you are going to Budapest!"

Tuky whispered *Modeh Ani*, stood up, and tried to straighten her rumpled dress. The boys got up, stretching and yawning, their backs stiff from lying on the hard, damp floor all night.

Tuky couldn't help feeling a bit excited to be going back to Budapest. Perhaps she could find her way back home or get into Apu's factory. In Budapest, maybe she would find an old friend or neighbor to help them... maybe Anna or Schober né!

One thing was certain; they could not ask the officer anything. He looked too stern.

The three children stood at the front desk, waiting to leave. They watched the officer sip his coffee and chew on a fresh, warm roll. Tuky was afraid to ask for something to eat, but how long could they go without food? Her stomach rumbled with hunger.

Before she could decide what to do, little Misu piped up.

"Could I have some?" he asked in a tiny voice. "We had no supper and no breakfast."

The officer frowned, but he handed Tuky a bag with another roll inside.

"Take this, and follow me," he said.

Outside, a younger officer was waiting for them. The children walked behind him all the way to the nearest train station. The conductor didn't give them a second glance as the young officer took them aboard for the first train ride of their young lives.

It was quite a different trip than driving in the wagon with Ladics bácsi, but to Tuky, it felt very much the same. It was a journey to the unknown. But with some bread to still their hunger, the boys couldn't help enjoying the ride.

Puncsi's eyes were shining as the train pulled out and gained speed. "Look how fast we're going!"

Misu was excited, too. He jumped up and down on the wooden seat.

"Don't," Tuky whispered, placing a warning hand on his shoulder.

She stared out the window at the passing countryside. Women were hanging clean laundry on the line to dry. Barefoot children played in the fields along the tracks. Everyone's life seemed to go on just as it always had. Didn't anyone care about three children who just wanted to go home?

Soon the houses were closer together and the train slowed.

"Next stop, Budapest!" called the conductor.

When they got off the train, Tuky searched the platform for a familiar face. Maybe their parents would come to pick them up. Maybe they would recognize a friend or a neighbor. But, all they saw were Nazi soldiers in shiny black boots, their large dogs barking at their sides.

They hurried along behind the young officer, trying not to get bumped in the crowded station. Tuky was scared and disappointed. Here they were in their own city, and they didn't see even a single Jew!

Tuky held onto the boys very tightly as they crossed the street where an army truck stood waiting. The young officer stretched out his right arm and saluted the German soldier behind the wheel.

"Here they are," he said, pointing to the children. By now, Tuky realized, they must look quite a sight. There hadn't been any soap and water in the cell last night, and they were bedraggled and pale.

"Load them in," said the soldier.

For a moment, Tuky wanted to grab the boys and run. They were small and fast, and maybe they could hide! The thought passed as quickly as it had come. *I can never find my way around a big city with two little boys.*

And what if we are separated? We need to stick together.

The officer hoisted them into the back of the truck. The children sat quietly as the truck started moving. Home seemed so far away, even though it was quite close by.

After a few minutes, the truck slowed, and the soldier saluted a guard standing near a large gate. Two soldiers ran over to open the gates, and the truck drove inside.

"What is this place?" Tuky wondered. There were rows and rows of buildings with courtyards, a lot of army trucks, and many, many soldiers with fierce looking dogs.

A sign on the main building said "Detention Center," but to Tuky, it seemed more like a jail. The gates were closed, and no one looked very happy. Tuky hoped that someone here would like children and be nice to them.

The driver brought the children into the office. The soldier behind the desk didn't even look up before he began questioning them:

"Name?"

"Mother's name?"

"Where are you from?"

"How old are you?"

With trembling voices, the children answered all the questions.

"You will stay here in the detention center until we can move you elsewhere," said the soldier to Tuky. "You will get one meal a day. You will follow instructions exactly."

"Boys this way; the girl goes over there."

Tuky couldn't believe it. She thought they would be together. How would her little brother and cousin fend for themselves? Tuky opened her mouth to protest, but she knew it wouldn't do any good. Instead, she poked Puncsi with her elbow.

"Take care of Misu," she whispered. "Make friends with the others, and do whatever they do."

One soldier led the boys to the men's quarters, and the other led Tuky out of the office and over to the women's area.

There were hundreds of women and girls milling around. Some were waiting in line for soup and bread. Tuky hoped to see a familiar face, but no one gave her a single glance. *What would happen to the boys? How would she ever find them again?*

There was no time to lose. Tuky began trying to figure out how this place worked. She roamed around the large, dusty courtyard. There were a few buildings, so she ducked into the nearest one. It was dark and dingy. The rooms were all the same, with bunkers from end to end.

A woman was leaving the block of buildings and heading toward the offices. This gave Tuky an idea. She walked closely behind the woman, trying to look as if she was her little girl. It might be useful to know where the offices were, and if there were some way of seeing the boys.

The woman kept to the side of the muddy path, walking with her head down. It was never good to look a Nazi soldier in the eye, or to annoy one of the dogs. It certainly made sense to stay out of the way of military trucks and cars.

Tuky looked carefully at the layout of the buildings. Although she saw some boys sitting near the men's fence, Misu and Puncsi were nowhere to be found.

The woman turned and entered a small building. Tuky peeked in and saw a sergeant at a desk. It was an office! Maybe she would hear some news. The little girl leaned against the wall and tried to look as if she belonged there.

The woman asked if she could send a letter, and the officer laughed at her. "Who would you send a letter to a Jew? There are none of your kind left in Hungary."

Tuky shivered. Surely that hateful soldier was wrong! But her heart sank as she made her way back to the women's bunkers. She was totally alone. Without her family, without the boys, and with no way of letting anyone else know where she was.

It was all too much for one day. Tuky swayed and leaned against the courtyard wall. She joined the line for food, and ate what she was given. When the women were herded indoors to sleep, she followed. Everyone lay down, packed together in the crowded space.

The little girl was exhausted, but sleep would not come.

"Are there really no Jews left anywhere outside this place?" she wondered. "Is there really no way to help anyone find me... find us?"

Tuky sighed in the darkness. Surely Apu would be searching for them when this war was over. She had to think of something.

After saying *Shema*, and closing her eyes, Tuky mind drifted. She could picture Apu's smile, Anyu's busy hands, Zsuzsa's little face... Suddenly, in a flash, she felt the beginning of an idea! There *was* something she could do, and she would start tomorrow!

Chapter Eleven

"Up, up, *schnell, schnell!*" The German women who patrolled the women's area woke everyone gruffly. Tuky straightened her dress, tied her shoes, and smoothed her hair the best she could. Today, she would take action. Today, maybe she would find her cousin and her little brother.

After davening whatever she could remember by heart, Tuky made her way around the courtyard and out to the path. She looked over toward the men's fenced in building, but again, no Misu, no Puncsi.

Tuky looked behind her before she entered the little office building. She walked up to the officer in charge, took a deep breath, and asked him, "Is there a package here for Gestetner Malka?"

The soldier glared at her. "A package for you, little Jew? Don't make me laugh! No one even knows you are here!"

The workers behind him smirked. But Tuky stood tall and answered as her Anyu had taught her to speak to adults.

"Thank you, sir."

Strangely satisfied, she carefully made her way back to the women's bunkers. Tuky's plan was underway.

❦ ❦ ❦

In this strange place, time seemed to stand still. One day was exactly like the next, and the days turned into weeks. There was nothing but concrete and the smell of diesel fuel around them. They couldn't leave the center, and even if they could, where would they go?

Rumors went around the camp, and Tuky didn't know which ones to believe. Would they all be sent to Germany by train? Would they be sent to work camps? Or, as others insisted, was the war almost over?

The food rations were only bread and watery soup. Tuky was always hungry, always searching for something – anything – to eat.

And each day, she picked her way down the muddy path to the main office. By now, all the workers knew exactly what she'd say.

"Is there a package here for Gestetner Malka?"

Of course, there never was.

Somehow, Tuky never looked disappointed. In spite of the jokes and even when they all laughed at her, she always smiled politely and thanked the officer in charge. She felt older and braver than when she'd left home.

Then, without warning, something did happen.

The women and girls were lined up for food, when the female guards began pulling some of them out of the line.

"*Schnell, schnell,* you and you!" They herded twenty prisoners into a corner, and Tuky knew this had to mean trouble.

Quickly, she stepped backward to avoid the guards. But in a second, she was pulled into the group and led out of the courtyard along with the rest.

"*Schnell, schnell!*" Tuky looked for somewhere to run and hide, but there simply wasn't anywhere to go. *What was this all about?*

The frightened women marched along the side of the building, down a flight of stairs, and into a dark cellar with a dirt floor. With every last one of them inside, the guards slammed the thick metal door and locked it.

It took a few minutes for her eyes to get used to the darkness in the room. Tuky shivered. She saw about thirty women already sitting on the floor, staring at the new arrivals. It seemed that she was the youngest one there.

A small, barred window provided a tiny sliver of light. Tuky carefully walked over to the window and sat down. She was already thinking of the boys, and hoping she would spot them through the window. *Even in here, I'm still in charge.*

A woman next to her leaned forward and peered closely at Tuky's face. She asked, "Are you a Gestetner from Budapest?"

Tuky looked up in surprise. "Yes," she answered. A warm feeling spread over her. It was so comforting that someone here knew her family. It had been so long since an adult was truly kind.

"I'm Tuky… I mean, Malka."

With tears in her eyes, the woman hugged the little girl. "I am Dushinski néni," she whispered, "your mother's friend. I was brought here with my husband, but I don't know where he's been taken."

Tuky clung to Dushinski néni. She tried to pretend she was hugging her very own beloved Anyu.

"What will happen to us?" asked Tuky.

Dushinski néni sighed. "Daven to Hashem, beautiful girl. Daven that this should all be over soon."

Day after day, Tuky sat in the cold, dim room with all the other Jewish women. Were they going to be punished? Would they be sent to Germany? Why were they here?

Once each afternoon, a guard would come in and bring them a bit of watery soup or stale bread. It was never enough to fill them up. Tuky's stomach growled with hunger.

Sometimes, the women talked about the food they used to cook for their families. Tuky could close her eyes and picture Anyu's soup with knaidelach, her fresh baked bread, crunchy radishes, and big cups of nourishing milk.

But when she opened her eyes, she was still sitting in the dark, damp cellar, and she was even hungrier than before.

Her mind grew dull and sleepy. There was nothing to break the boredom of all the dreary hours. Tuky forced herself to stand by the small cellar window hoping she might see

Puncsi and Misu. The window was level with the dusty ground outside, but all she ever saw were the legs and feet of soldiers walking past.

Late one afternoon, as she stood in her usual place, Tuky saw two sets of small legs and feet passing by. The shoes on those little feet were scuffed and dusty, but somehow, they looked familiar. Tuky wasn't sure she could believe her eyes.

"Puncsi? Misu?" she called, "I'm here; I'm here!"

The two boys turned around and ran to the cellar window. They sat down on the ground and stuck their legs through the bars. Tuky hugged their legs tightly. It was a miracle that they had found each other!

She noticed their loose, dragging shoelaces and smiled. There was work to do! Tuky was still in charge.

"Where have you two been?" she asked.

"With all the men and boys," they answered. "You are close to where we sleep."

Misu looked through the bars hopefully. "Do you have any food? We're starving."

Tuky shook her head. She had no food for the boys, but she felt a new energy and hope. It was if her brain was waking up.

"Did you daven today?" asked Tuky.

"Not really," said Misu.

"Just let me fix these laces, and we'll start."

With the boys' shoes neatly tied, Tuky softly began saying *Modeh Ani,* and any other *tefillah* she could remember. As the sky turned darker, Tuky kissed them and told them to go back, before the soldiers started patrolling.

"Come back here tomorrow! And don't forget to say *Shema* before you go to sleep!"

The boys waved goodbye and scampered off, and Tuky smiled and waved back. At least now she knew her brother and her cousin were safe!

Tuky lay down that night feeling thankful. She whispered the *Shema* and fell asleep.

🌷 🌷 🌷

For the next few days, the boys returned to visit Tuky at her tiny window. This was the best part of the day for all three of them. They would talk a little, daven together, and of course Tuky would tie the boys' shoelaces.

Their lives had a pattern, and although they had nothing else, the children had each other.

Tuky was standing at the window one day, waiting for Misu and Puncsi to arrive, when a German truck pulled right up near the building.

"It's not time for our food," Tuky thought. "I wonder what's going on."

The door to the cellar clanged open. The women squinted in the bright light, startled and afraid. A Nazi guard stood in the doorway shouting, "Everyone stand up! Quickly, *schnell!* Into the truck! Time to go!"

Tuky's heart began to race. As bad as this place was, how could she leave it?

If I get into that truck, who will take care of the little boys? Will they send us to another country? How will Apu ever find me?

Every step along the way, Tuky had

done what she was told. She had kept quiet. She had felt shy and uncertain. Her heart was thumping. What should she do?

Tuky looked around frantically for the rabbi's wife. Would it be safer and better to follow her into the truck? As all the women filed out the door, Dushinski néni bent down and whispered, "Do not leave this place."

So that was her answer. But now what? In seconds, she would be forced to leave. She was the last one in the cellar.

"Oh, Hashem! Please help me," she whispered.

Where the idea came from, the little girl never knew, but Tuky didn't waste a minute.

Bravely, she walked right up to the guard at the door, and took a deep breath. In her sweetest, most charming voice, she said, "Please, sir! My two little brothers are here without their father, without their mother! I can't go, or there will be no one to take care of them."

The guard actually took a moment to look down at Tuky's thin, pale face.

She stared back at him, thinking frantically.

Desperately, she added, "They're so small; they can't even tie their own shoes!"

The Nazi didn't answer her. Why would he even care about her and the boys? Nobody had cared for so long.

Tuky held her breath. She felt her heart thumping in her chest. *Please! Please!*

The guard shrugged his shoulders. He looked around to make sure no one was watching.

Then, swiftly, he motioned for Tuky to stand behind the open door. Anyone who checked the cellar would see an empty room.

Tuky stood completely still in her hiding place. She could hear the doors of the truck slamming. She could hear the roar of the engine as the truck drove away. She could almost hear her own heart beating in the silence.

When the truck was gone, the guard led Tuky up the concrete steps. She marched behind his shiny black boots, taking long steps to keep up. Could it be? Had he really saved her, or was she in even more trouble?

The guard stopped in front of a metal building that said, "Personnel Only." Was something good or something terrible behind the door? Tuky had no way of knowing, but it was too late now. She stepped into the building, and what a sight met her eyes!

A bunch of soldiers were sitting around, eating apple strudel. Tuky's eyes popped. She hadn't seen anything so delicious in weeks and weeks!

The guard laughed and joked with the other men. He cut a big piece of the beautiful cake and set it in front of the hungry little girl. Tuky made a *brocha* and wolfed it down. She was full of strudel and full of joy. She'd been saved!

When she was finished eating, the guard opened the door and said, "All right, kid.

Make sure no one knows that you were ever in that cellar. Now, scram!"

Tuky ran as fast as her legs could carry her. She had to find the boys. Out in the fresh air she raced around the detention center, searching for Misu and Puncsi. Finally, there they were, playing with some pebbles and sticks in the mud.

She stopped right in front of them, and they looked up in shock. The three children hugged each other and laughed. How happy they were to be together once again!

"Come on," said Tuky. "Come with me!"

The boys scampered after her, along the path and into the post office. They stared at Tuky as she walked up to the desk and asked, "Is there a package here for Gestetner Malka?"

The officer in charge didn't even look up. "Get out!" he yelled.

The new Tuky, the one who didn't feel shy anymore, didn't even mind. She said 'thank you' in her usual way, and the children left in a hurry.

"What do you think you're doing?" asked Puncsi.

Tuky just smiled confidently and answered, "You'll see."

Chapter Twelve

After Tuky was freed from the cellar, things in the camp seemed different. Could the war be coming to an end?

Some people had actually received packages in the detention center. The children took that as a good sign. There were fewer Nazi soldiers and trucks around. The guards all seemed to be very preoccupied, too busy to be as strict as they had before.

Tuky knew without a doubt that her Apu would come and get her and the boys someday. But when would that be?

They tried to manage with the little they had. But, the hunger was terrible! It kept them company in the morning when they woke up. It was with them all day. And at night, they would lie awake, feeling that hollow emptiness inside. The stale bread and thin, watery soup they got once a day just didn't satisfy them.

Tuky did whatever she could to find extra food for herself and the boys. She hung around the garbage pails behind the camp kitchen. Sometimes there were potato peels or scraps of food to be found. The children would eat anything at all to quiet their hunger.

One day, while Tuky was hiding near the back door of the kitchen, she noticed a truck load of bread being delivered. She couldn't take her eyes off the precious bread. She was so worried about the boys; they needed to eat more.

Suddenly, as the kitchen worker hoisted a tray of bread over his shoulder, one loaf fell and rolled to the side. Tuky didn't care that it had fallen on the ground. She dashed over and hid it under her apron. Looking around frantically, she crouched behind the kitchen wall, breathing hard. When the truck driver started the motor, Tuky ran off. She could barely speak when she found Puncsi and Misu. She just pulled the bread from under her apron and watched the boys' eyes light up.

What a feast they had that day! For the first time in a while, the children were full. They finished every last crumb of that bread, and thanked Hashem for helping them.

Another time, she wasn't so successful. On her usual search for food, she discovered a bunch of carrots behind the garbage pail. As she scooped it up and tried to get away, one of the female kitchen workers grabbed Tuky's hand.

"Oh, no, you don't!" said the woman. Tuky let go of the carrots, realizing that the worker would probably keep them for herself.

"Maybe I'll find more food tomorrow," thought Tuky. And then she was off to the camp office for her daily visit. She marched straight in.

"Good day. My name is Gestetner Malka. I am waiting for a package. Did it arrive yet?"

The guard shook his head. Perhaps he had started feeling a bit sorry for this little girl because the package she asked for every day about was never there.

"Hey, you. Wait. Take this," he said.

Surprised, Tuky reached out and took a package of biscuits that he gave her. She thanked him happily and ran to show Misu and Puncsi the unexpected treat.

Almost every day the boys would ask her when they could go home.

"Soon," Tuky always answered. "Soon Apu will come looking for us, and he'll take us out of here."

Weeks passed. One day, as Tuky stepped into the little office, she heard loud voices. Nervously, she poked her head inside. There was a Hungarian man in a short dark jacket, arguing with the Nazi guard there. When they saw her, they grew quiet.

The officer in charge looked at her, and said, "Go get your brothers and come right back."

Tuky turned around and ran to get them. *Oh, Hashem! What now?* As she searched for the boys, she tried hard to think what they might have done wrong. *Are we going to be punished?*

When they returned, the officer told the man, "There they are! Those are the Gestetner children you're asking for, and you can have them!"

"How do you know?" asked the man. "How do you know their name?"

The guard seemed upset. "How do I know their name? How do I know that name? Because she," he pointed at Tuky, "bothered me every single day… asking for a package for Gestetner Malka. I'll never forget that name as hard as I try!"

The boys looked at Tuky in admiration. Now they understood what she had been doing all this time! She smiled back at them, her heart singing with joy. Apu discovered they had been taken from the farm. He sent someone to search for them, and now they were found!

"Clever girl," said the man. "Your Apu paid me well to look for you three. As a sign that I am his messenger, your Apu told me your nickname is 'Tuky.' Now, come with me." The children followed him to a big black car.

Could it finally be? Tuky felt as if she were in a dream, riding in the car, out of the gates of the detention center... away from the soldiers, and the hunger, and the lonely nights.

As they drove down the streets of Budapest, she looked out the window. When would she see the familiar sights of her neighborhood? Tuky tried not to blink so she wouldn't miss that first glimpse of the vinegar tree, and the gravel-lined road toward her home.

It was Puncsi who first realized.

"This isn't the way home," he blurted out.

"No," said the man. "It's not safe to go there. Your family has taken refuge in some houses owned by a different country. For now, these Swedish houses are safe from the Nazis. Your parents are waiting for you there."

He drove the car toward the Danube River and stopped at a road block. The guards questioned him, and then waved the car through.

Tuky tried to brush the dirt off her shoes. She wiped Misu's face with her apron. What would it be like to see everyone after such a long time?

The car pulled up to a row of beautiful buildings, and the man led the children inside. They followed him up a fancy staircase and down a narrow hallway. Tuky could feel her heart beating fast. It had been so long and so difficult. She could barely swallow.

As the boys ran ahead to knock at the door, it opened suddenly. And there, with the light shining behind him, was Apu! He looked thinner, and older, but it was their beloved father.

"Could it be?" he whispered.

Apu bent down and hugged the boys. "Hashem was watching over you," he kept saying. "Hashem brought you back to us."

Tears were flowing down his face, and Tuky longed to hug him. But first, she stepped back and took out her coin necklace. There was something important she had to say.

"I always remembered that I was a Jewish girl, Apu. I never forgot it for one moment!"

Apu reached out and held Tuky close against his heart. Tuky didn't want her father to ever let go of her. She cried and cried for the many lonely and scary months apart.

Apu pulled the three children into the room, and announced, "Look at the presents I received today!"

Familiar faces surrounded them. There was Anyu, and Tuky's two older sisters, her brothers, and... could those big children really be Szuza and Miki? Her aunt and uncle and all her cousins crowded around. Both families had survived – every single one of them. How they hugged and cried! It felt so good, so miraculous, to be together again.

Apu looked at his daughter proudly. The gold in his smile winked at her.

"You are such a big girl. You took good care of the boys, I can see."

Tuky nodded. "I tried to," she said simply. "But it was really Hashem who took care of all of us. He is really the One in charge."

Epilogue

Six years after Budapest was liberated and her family had been reunited, Tuky stood on the deck of the S.S. Olympia. She craned her neck to see the shore of Canada, the country that would be her new home. Anyu, Apu, Tuky's brothers and sisters, her uncle, aunt, and their entire family had all survived those frightening, dangerous times. It was nothing short of miraculous!

The family after the war

After the war, in January of 1945, Anyu had a baby boy named Zigi. The family then returned to their old home, but none of their belongings were left. Anyu's Shabbos candlesticks were gone, and the factory was empty. Even Tuky's handkerchief, the one she'd embroidered with such care, had been taken. However, the vinegar tree she loved so much had survived, and was still flourishing in the courtyard on Kolozsvari Street.

Strangely, the coins blessed by the Belzer Rebbe and treasured throughout the war, had all disappeared. One by one, each family member had lost or misplaced the precious coins. The blessing had been fulfilled, and their work was done.

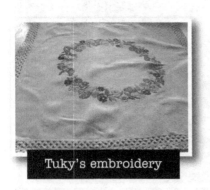
Tuky's embroidery

There was more good news in store for the family. Anyu went on to have a baby girl named Zisi, and Apu obtained Canadian visas for everyone!

While waiting for the big move to Montreal, Tuky embroidered a colorful tablecloth with beautiful flowers.

What would life be like for them in a new country with a different language and unfamiliar ways? Although no one knew exactly what to expect, one thing was certain: they had each other, and they had the Torah to guide them as they started all over again.

The journey by ship took two weeks. After the first few days of feeling seasick, the children actually began to enjoy the trip. They played games and had meals together. Tuky's older sister, Mirca, went daily to the ship's

In the ship's dining room

kitchen to supervise the chefs as they cooked the kosher food.

A few weeks after settling in Montreal, Anyu was blessed with another baby. Little Ezriel was the eleventh child born to the Gestetner Family. Apu opened a factory, and once again, Tuky's home was a haven to everyone in need. In this new land, Apu continued being a *mohel*. He performed thousands of *brissin* in his life, never taking money for the service. Tuky's two older sisters, Hindi and Mirca, were married.

The family in Montreal

Then, one Friday night during the Shabbos meal, Apu suddenly passed away. What a calamity! An immigrant family – only four years after arriving in Canada – left without their beloved father. Anyu had to continue on her own. After the seven days of *shiva*, she went to work in the factory to support her family. When they were old enough, the boys continued and expanded the business.

Anyu lived to the ripe old age of 93, saying Tehillim in her every free moment. Her *emunah* and good cheer continue to inspire her children, grandchildren and great-grand children to this very day.

Tuky at her wedding

Being the oldest girl at home, Tuky helped her mother run the house and take care of the younger children. She married Shaya Treitel, a fine young

Lubavitcher Chossid from Czechoslovakia who was living in Montreal. Tuky's children and her family were always most important to her, and she made caring for them her career.

Tuky (yes, she's had the same nickname all her life) has always been willing to share the miraculous story of her survival with family, friends, groups of students, and now – through this book – with you! On the day her first great-grandchild was born, Tuky decided to see if she could still stand on her head.

She could, and she did!

Historical Note

Historical Note

The word "holocaust" means destruction. The Holocaust, one of the most terrible events in recent memory, took place during World War II. A man named Adolph Hitler (*yimach shemo*, may his name be erased) was the leader of Germany. He felt that the Germans were better than anyone else. He and his followers, called Nazis, dreamed of a world completely under their control.

The Nazi soldiers marched in and took over many countries in Europe. One by one, Austria, Czechoslovakia, Poland, Denmark, Norway, France, Luxembourg, the Netherlands, and Belgium were put under Nazi rule. Other countries, like Italy and Hungary, joined the German side in the war.

Like Haman in his day, Hitler was

determined to get rid of all the Jews. He was so sure he would succeed, that his officers took pictures of Jewish people and kept Jewish objects. They thought that eventually, the only place to find out about Jews would be in a museum with these items displayed.

Hitler's evil plan went in stages. First, the Nazis passed laws preventing Jews from holding jobs in the government. Then Jews were excluded from certain schools. Jewish doctors could not treat non-Jewish patients. Eventually, the laws prevented Jews from earning a living.

All over the land, Jewish teachers and workers were fired from their jobs. Every Jew – man, woman, and child – had to sew a yellow felt badge, shaped like a Jewish star, on their clothing. Their passports were stamped with a "J" to identify them as Jews.

When the Nazis took over countries like Poland and Hungary, they forced all the Jewish people into one area of town. This was called a ghetto. It had a wall and barbed wire around it and was guarded to prevent people from going in or out. The ghetto was crowded. There was little food or medicine. While Jews grew ill and hungry in the ghetto, the Germans took over all the beautiful Jewish homes, factories and businesses left behind. They stole valuables like silver, artwork, money, and jewelry.

The Nazis rounded up Jews, and sent them by train to places called concentration camps. Only people who were strong enough to work were kept alive, and often not for long. Hitler and his evil followers kept thinking of better and better ways to get rid of Jews and of Yiddishkeit. They took pleasure in making Jewish people eat on Yom Kippur and in destroying holy books and Torah scrolls.

Even though it was against the law to hide a Jew or help one escape, some brave non-Jewish men and women risked their lives and the lives of their families to do so. Out of the goodness of their hearts, they took in Jewish children and pretended they were part of their family. Others hid Jews in their barns, attics, or cellars. Sometimes, as in Tuky's story, the families that hid Jews were paid well for their help.

In spite of Nazi cruelty, Jewish people kept mitzvos even in the worst and hardest times. There are countless stories of how they continued to daven in secret, to put on a hidden pair of tefillin, or to review Torah by heart. They may have been hungry and cold and frightened, but they continued to serve Hashem with strong devotion... just like Tuky and her family.

Interview

Mrs. Tuky Treitel (left) with her daughter, Shterni

The Tuky in this book is a real person: Mrs. Tuky (Gestetner) Treitel, my mother!

In order to write her story, I asked a lot of questions, and I felt that hearing the answers of the grown-up Tuky would be of great interest to young readers.

Shterni (Treitel) Rosenfeld

Shterni Rosenfeld: Ma, so many other people who lived through the war never talked about what happened to them. Why did you decide to share your story?

Mrs. Tuky Treitel: After the war some people wanted to bury their pain. They felt that if they would not talk about their experiences, the sad feelings would go away.

My story was and is always with me. I felt it was important for you to know how valuable and precious life is and to appreciate it. One can rise above adversity.

S.R: How did your experience affect your relationship with Hashem and your commitment to Yiddishkeit?

T.T: I saw that we are all in Hashem's Hands. Hashem puts a person in the right place at the right time. The lesson of the *bentched* pengö coins which we all wore on silver chains, remains with me until today. My parents had great *emunas tzaddikim*. Seeing the *brocha* of the Belzer Rebbe be fulfilled was a living example of my upbringing.

S. R: It's so hard to imagine that you were so young when you were put into such a difficult situation. How did you find the strength and the maturity to be in charge of Puncsi and Misu?

T.T: I can't believe that I did this at the age of 6 ½ years old. We were taught to follow instructions; we had tremendous *kabolas ohl* (obedience). My father told us that we were to go with this stranger, (Editor: to save their lives) and that is what we did. No crying or carrying on.

At that point, being the oldest of the three, I realized that I had to take charge in order to survive. I visited the boys in the houses they were staying in daily. I tried to remind them to say *brochos* and *Shema*. I felt responsible for them.

S.R: When you returned to Budapest thirteen years ago, did you go and visit your old home?

T.T: When I went back, together with Anyu and some of my siblings, there was no time to go. We spent most of the time visiting the cemeteries. Our house has since been demolished and replaced by an apartment building.

S.R: You had to do a lot of sharing when you were a child. Many times you would go to sleep in your bed and wake up in the morning on a blanket on the floor because a guest had arrived. How did your parents demand this level of *Ahavas Yisroel* from you?

T.T: *Ahavas Yisroel* was not a word I ever heard from my parents. It was what they did, not what they discussed. My parents lived and breathed this *middah*. Their heart and home was open to anyone in need. From the people living in smaller towns seeking medical services in the hospitals or clinics of Budapest, to friends, relatives, or anyone seeking a place to stay or a warm meal, all were welcome.

S.R: How do you think your experiences as a child affected you in making you the kind of person that you are now?

T.T: When I grew up, children were meant to be seen and not heard. Before the war, I was more of a quiet child. When I was sent away with the two younger children, all of a sudden I had to take charge. This experience, although difficult, made me into the person I am today.

Glossary

Ahavas Yisroel - Loving a fellow Jew

Becher - Cup, often made of silver, used to hold the wine for Kiddush

Bentch - Bless

Bentching - A word used to refer to the blessing of thanks after eating a meal or blessing someone

Boruch Hashem - An expression meaning, "Thank G-d"

Brissin - Circumcisions

Brocha - Blessing

Challah (challos, pl.) - Bread baked in honor of the Sabbath

Cholent - A stew cooked before the Sabbath and kept warm overnight for the lunch meal

Chossid - Follower of a particular Chassidic movement

Daven (davening) - Pray (praying)

Elul - Last month before the Jewish New Year

Emunah - Faith; belief

Emunas tzaddikim - Faith in righteous (leaders)

Gut Shabbos - A greeting exchanged on the Sabbath; "Good Shabbos"

Hamotzi - Blessing recited over bread

Hashem - Literally, "The Name;" a respectful way of referring to G-d

Hashem Yisborach - G-d, blessed be He

Kiddush - Benediction recited over wine on the Sabbath and Jewish holidays

Mezuzah - Parchment scroll with handwritten text of the Shema, affixed to the doorposts of Jewish homes and buildings

Middah - Character trait

Mitzvah (mitzvos, pl.) - Good deed(s); one of the 613 commandments in the Torah

Modeh Ani - Prayer of thanks recited upon awakening

Mohel - One who performs circumcisions

Negel vasser - Ritual hand washing

Pesach - Passover

Reb - Courtesy title used before a man's first name

Schnell - German word meaning, "Quickly"

Shabbos - Sabbath

Shabbos Kodesh - The holy Sabbath

Shalom Aleichem - "Peace be unto you;" the opening words of a prayer recited on Friday night

Shema - The 'Hear O Israel' Prayer

Shiva - Week of mourning

Shul - Synagogue

Siddur (siddurim, pl.) - Prayer book(s)

Tefillah - Prayer

Teffillin - Phylacteries

Tzaddik - Righteous person

Tzedokah - Charity

Yiddishkeit - Judaism

Yom Kippur - Day of Atonement

Zemiros - Songs sung on the Sabbath

About the Photos

Page 157: The family after the war
Back row, from left to right: Apu, Anyu, Mirca, Sami, Tuky, Misu
Bottom row, left to right: Zsuzsa, Frédi, Miki, Zigi, Zisi
(Hindi was already married and is not in this picture,
or the one on page 159.)

Page 159: In the ship's dining room
At the head of the table: Apu, Anyu
To Anyu's right, continuing around the table:
Mirca, Tuky, Zsuzsa, Zisi, Zigi, Miki, Frédi, Misu, Sami

Page 160: The family in Montreal
(Last picture before Apu passed away)
Back row, left to right:
Zsuzsa, Anshel Itzkowits (Mirca's husband) Sami, Miki,
Misu (with hat), Frédi, Lipi Braun (Hindi's husband)
Front row, left to right:
Zisi, Mirca, Apu, holding Eizik Braun (Hindi's oldest son) Anyu,
holding Ezriel, Hindi, holding her son Nattie Braun, Zigi (with cap)

Enjoy all these exciting books for young readers from Hachai Publishing!

Israel in the days of
King Chizkiyahu

Israel in the days of
the Maccabees

Spain • 1492

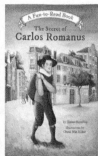

Amsterdam/Spain • 1650

Eastern Europe • 1800's

Russia • 1853

North Dakota • 1897

New York • 1905

WWI • Poland • 1914

Baltimore • 1930

WWII • Hungary • 1944

Toronto, Canada • 1946

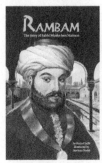

Spain/Egypt • 1100's

Story Collection

Story Collection

America • present day